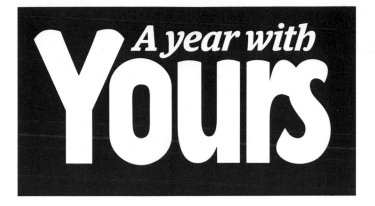

A year with
Yours

Name	
Address	
Postcode	
Home phone	
Mobile phone	
Email	

In case of emergency, contact:

Name	
Telephone	

USEFUL CONTACTS

BANK	
BUILDING SOCIETY	
CHEMIST/PHARMACY	
CHIROPODIST	
COUNCIL	
CREDIT CARD EMERGENCY	
DENTIST	
DOCTOR	
ELECTRICIAN	
GARAGE	
HAIRDRESSER	
HOSPITAL	
LOCAL POLICE	
MILKMAN	
OPTICIAN	
PLUMBER	
SOLICITOR	
TAXI	
VET	

RENEWAL REMINDERS

	RENEWAL DATE	POLICY NUMBER	TELEPHONE
CAR INSURANCE			
CAR TAX			
MOT			
HOME INSURANCE			
TV LICENCE			
PET INSURANCE			
Yours SUBSCRIPTION			

THE YEAR AHEAD

Why we love...
Spring

After the long, dark winter months, the arrival of spring comes as a breath of fresh air. The spring equinox (March 20) brings lighter, longer days and a little more sunshine, signalling that winter is receding and the delights of Easter are just around the corner. Nature bursts back to life with an exciting explosion of sight, sound and smell as plants bud, trees blossom and bulbs push through the earth to reveal their glorious colour. Hedgehogs and dormice begin to awaken from their slumber, foraging around the newly abundant supply of food the season brings. Feathered friends become busy finding mates, building nests and defending territories during the breeding season, bringing a crescendo of birdsong which fills the sweetly scented air. Towards the end of the season, when singing species have returned from their migratory trail, the dawn chorus can be heard in full swing - the perfect serenade on an early morning stroll.

POND LIFE

Nothing signals spring like a mass of clear jelly with little black dots jostling about in pond water. As soon as the temperatures begin to rise, adult frogs and toads will come out of hibernation to breed - but a single cold snap can spell disaster!

EYE-CATCHING COLOUR

A carpet of Lesser Celandine flowers are a joy to see on any walk. Characterised by their bright star-shaped yellow petals and glossy green heart-shaped leaves, you can spot these flowers blooming along hedgerows, woodlands and in parks from March onwards.

PIC: SHUTTERSTOCK

WOOLLY JUMPERS

Newborn lambs are one of the earliest signs of spring, frolicking on farms and fields all across the country. As they grow in size, so does their confidence and curiosity, venturing further afield to play and explore until the ewe bleats for them to return.

WONDROUS WATERFALLS

The volume of water from April showers turns calm flowing waterfalls into thundering torrents, creating a crescendo of noise - making this the perfect time to witness their displays. From the Brecon Beacons to the Lake District, the UK is not short of places to witness these dashing displays.

It's a beautiful day!

A SPRING IN YOUR STEP

There's ample opportunity to step through a golden carpet at this time of year as flocks of daffodils raise their drowsy little heads into the spring sunshine. You can find vistas of the beauties all over the UK, but the Lake District has to offer one of the most spectacular daffodil sights. After all, even the daffodil poet himself William Wordsworth was known to have a soft spot for this rural idyll. Root yourself at Lake Windermere or Coniston Water for the best views, but make it your business to tour as much of the area and call into as many honeypot towns as you can while the tourist crowds aren't about.

PICTURE POSTCARD

The whimsical-looking cottages and beautiful countryside of The Cotswolds always look like they've been plucked straight from the cover of a pretty chocolate box, but in spring this Area of Outstanding Natural Beauty is extra special. Here the woodlands burst into colour, gardens bloom and the meadows spring to life with frolicking lambs. Keen walkers can blow away the cobwebs by taking on any part of the 100-mile Cotswold Way which passes countless charming villages and pubs. Bourton-on-Water is one of the most picturesque villages, nicknamed the Venice of the Cotswolds as the River Windrush flows right through the centre of town. Or for something completely different, join in with one of Britain's best wacky traditions at the Gloucestershire Cheese Rolling held each May which sees competitors hurtle a 7lb Double Gloucester – and themselves – down Cooper's Hill in Brockworth.

HEAR THE DAWN CHORUS

Morning larks are in for a treat as first light brings with it a whole symphony of sound. From March to July, our feathered alarm clocks sing their hearts out to defend their territories and attract a mate. Robins and great tits tend to start the choir off early in the season, joined later by their chiffchaff and blackcap friends, before May and June sees everyone belting out in harmony. The RSPB hosts dawn chorus walks around the country (call 01767 680551 or visit rspb. org.uk/reserves-and-events) or for something extra special take a trip to Blakeney Point in Norfolk where you'll be spoiled with a coastal chorus from swallows, sand martins and meadow pipits. **Visit nationaltrust.org.uk/blakeney-national-nature-reserve**

ALL ABOARD

Experience all the thrill of Yorkshire's most majestic hills and valleys, without any of the sore feet or risk of April showers, by hopping on board the Settle to Carlisle railway. Weave through a patchwork of lush green valleys, stitched together by higgledy-piggledy stone walls and, with a cup of Yorkshire tea in hand, drink in the best views of the Yorkshire Three Peaks, the Eden valley and the fine sandstone city of Carlisle. Go by steam train for a truly unforgettable experience. **Call 03457 484950 or visit nationalrail.co.uk**

3 OF THE BEST... QUIRKY MUSEUMS

Step into the wacky and wonderful and learn something totally new in one of Britain's kookiest museums.

◆ The Land of Lost Content Museum in Shropshire is an Aladdin's cave of nostalgia, celebrating everyday items from ordinary people's lives through the decades. It features everything from the sweets we bought as children to what you'd find in a Sixties kitchen and old-fashioned cosmetics. **Call 01588 676176 or visit lolc.co.uk**

PIC: SHUTTERSTOCK

◆ WOW! WHAM! KAPOW! Let the Cartoon Museum in Holborn, London, take you back to childhood days with displays of the best of British cartoons and comic art. There are collections from the 18th Century to today, including the memorable antics of much-loved favourites Billy Whizz and Dennis the Menace. **Call 0207 580 8155 or visit cartoonmuseum.org**

◆ It's always time for a brew at Teapot Island in Kent, a museum that holds the Guinness World Record for the biggest collection of teapots of all shapes and sizes including rare designs such as Princess Diana and Doctor Who teapots. While there, try your hand at some teapot pottery yourself or treat yourself to a warm scone and steaming pot of tea. **Call 01622 814541 or visit teapotisland.co.uk**

Luscious leaves

Add a touch of cool elegance to your garden with these shade-loving, sculptural foliage plants, says Louise Curley

All gardens need fabulous foliage to add structure, texture and interest, and hostas are one of the best leafy plants you can grow. They're perennials that die down in winter then re-emerge in spring when slender, pointy buds poke up above ground. These buds gradually unfurl, revealing leaves that are teardrop-shaped, although some have longer, more slender foliage. The leaves have a tactile, ribbed texture that captures droplets of moisture, which glisten on the leaves.

Hostas are shade-loving plants so they are perfect for dark, damp woodland-style flower beds and, because they love moist soil, they'll also thrive at the edge of ponds. In small gardens or on a shady terrace, grow hostas in containers filled with a compost for mature plants (Westland John

Innes No.3 compost, £4.99/30 litres, homebase. co.uk) and water frequently with a full can to make sure they don't dry out – every other day and sometimes daily in hot weather. They will need repotting every few years. These stunning plants come in a range of greens, from bluey-greys to yellowy tones, and some are variegated with creamy-white edges to the leaves or flashes of yellow. There is also a range of sizes. Miniature hostas such as 'Blue Mouse Ears' grow to only 10-12cm (4-5in) in height, whereas giant hostas such as 'Blue Mammoth' can make clumps about 1m (3ft) tall, so bear in mind the eventual size and allow plenty of room for the hosta to grow. The miniatures are best planted in containers or raised beds where they won't get swamped by other plants and can be admired close-up.

HOW TO GROW HOSTAS IN THE GROUND

These plants are really easy to grow as long as you can give them plenty of food and water.

Weed the area where you're going to plant your hostas, then dig in plenty of compost or well-rotted manure (we can recommend Verve Horse Manure Soil Improver, £4.37/50 litres, diy.com). This will add nutrients to the soil and help hold moisture around the roots, especially during the dry summer months.

Hostas are best planted in spring so that the roots have had a chance to establish before summer, or in autumn, which gives them time to settle in before the weather gets cold. Plant them somewhere shady – dappled shade under deciduous trees is ideal but most hostas can cope with deeper shade, which is why they're such useful plants. Dig a hole for each hosta twice the width but the same depth as the pot it comes in.

Gently tip out the hosta and place it in the hole. Fill in around the sides with soil and firm the plant in place using your hands. Use a full can to water each one. Make sure they are kept moist over the coming months, especially during dry spells.

Slugs and snails are the biggest problem when it comes to growing hostas. These creatures are especially fond of the fresh growth, so it's important to protect new buds when they appear in spring. They are most active when the ground is wet and at night, so go on patrol after a rain shower or as the sun goes down. Pick up any that you find and pop them in a bucket of salty water.

Organic slug pellets (Growing Success Advanced Organic Slug Killer, £6.99, marshalls-seeds.co.uk) won't harm wildlife such as birds and hedgehogs, but are very effective at keeping slugs at bay. Scatter the pellets sparingly and evenly over the soil rather than creating big piles of them in one spot, and use them early in the year before plants have started to grow. Scatter the pellets over the soil every week from February onwards and they will catch slugs emerging after winter.

THREE LUSH-LEAVED HOSTAS TO TRY

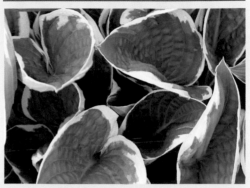

'FRANCEE'
An elegant hosta with heart-shaped green leaves and crisp white edges. £9.99 crocus.co.uk

'WHIRLWIND'
Thick, textured leaves with a gentle twist. Pale green centres and olive edges. £5.50 dorsetperennials.co.uk

'EL NINO'
Medium-sized hosta with blue/green leaves and white edging. £5.50 dorsetperennials.co.uk

Indoor window

MATERIALS:
Old rectangular wooden box
Cream paint
Empty cans
Scraps of linen fabric
Embroidery floss (thread)
Buttons (optional)
Old newspaper or printed paper
Fresh flowers, spring bulbs, or fresh herbs in pots

TOOLS:
Paintbrush
Needle
Pencil
Scissors
Spring motif templates
Cookie cutters (optional)
White craft (PVA) glue

box

Fill your window box with cut flowers or fresh herbs with this pretty decoupage project

1 Make sure the surface of your box is clean and dry and then paint it, inside and out, with cream paint. You may need to add a second coat so allow to dry between coats. Do the same with the empty cans.

2 Cut a few small rectangles from the linen fabric. Using a needle and stranded embroidery floss (thread), stitch a motif onto each one. Choose spring motifs such as flowers, chicks, or little wreaths. You only need a few to give the box its own unique character. Add a few small buttons here and there if you have some to hand.

3 Use a pencil to draw various shapes onto the newspaper, such as ducks, hearts, and rabbits. If you have some shaped cookie cutters to hand, use those.

4 Glue the various embellishments onto the box, not forgetting the ends. Give the cans a touch of decoration as well, then fill with fresh flowers or herbs. This window box looks equally delightful on a mantle or shelf.

Seasonal Scandi Crafts by Christiane Bellstedt Myers, published by CICO Books (£12.99) Photography by Caroline Arber © CICO Books

Why we love...
Summer

Summer is the season when nature is at its busiest best with sensational sights, smells and sounds all around. Just pottering about the garden can be a feast for the senses, inhaling the aroma from blooming flowers and freshly cut grass, listening to the faint buzz of insects whizzing around and watching the impressive acrobatics of swifts and swallows in the blue skies above. With its warmer climes, the season also provides the perfect opportunity to gather with friends and family for a spot of al-fresco dining – whether it be laying out a cream tea spread in the mid-afternoon, firing up the barbecue for dinner when the sun sets, or packing a picnic to enjoy under the leafy canopy of a tree at the park. And let's not forget about those spontaneous trips to the seaside, where trying our hands at building sandcastles and eating ice-creams before they melt are all just part of the fun.

PICS: ALAMY

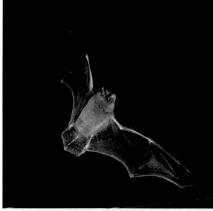

EVENING ACRO-BAT-ICS

On a dry summer's evening, just after sunset, look upwards and you'll be rewarded with the sight of bats filling the sky, whizzing around catching insects. They have a very big appetite and can eat thousands in just one night.

SUMMERTIME SPORTS

The distinctive sound of leather on willow, the cricket whites and the serving of tea and scones at half-time create the typical summertime scene of the village cricket match - a quintessential British tradition that's still going strong today.

BOUNTIFUL BLOOMS

An array of different flower shapes, patterns, colours and scents can be admired at this time of year, from pungent elderflowers, dog roses and towering foxgloves, to the yellow bird's-foot trefoil, pink bindweed, ox-eye daisies and rare orchids.

DYNAMIC DISPLAYS

Bees aren't the only insects to look out for at this time of year. You'll often find damselflies and dragonflies near bodies of water, whose wings can be heard rattling across the reeds and rushes as they dart about, doing impressive aerodynamic stunts.

Here comes the sun

WATERWAY WANDERS

Summer is the most glorious time to make the most of Britain's unique and historic canals. Telling the stories of decades of industry, in recent years many have had a new lease of life given to them and are a perfect spot for a refreshing summer stroll. The Llangollen Canal in Wales takes in the most impressive feats of engineering and nature from the Horseshoe Falls to the aqueduct known as a 'stream through the skies'. Or if you fancy enjoying the canals at an even steadier pace, consider chugging through the scenery on a canal boat. There are many opportunities to do this around the country – we love the pretty Avon Ring, which will see you pootle past picturesque mills, Shakespeare's Stratford-upon-Avon and through the longest flight of locks in Britain. To find out more about your local canal **call 0303 040 4040 or visit canalrivertrust.org.uk**

BERRY GOOD FUN

Pick a sunny day to visit one of the UK's wonderful pick-your-own (PYO) farms where you can fill your wicker basket with messy, juicy berries and crunchy veg. Most cost nothing or very little to visit and could work out cheaper than a trip to the supermarket. Ansty PYO and Farm Shop in Salisbury, Wiltshire, is a lovely family-run farm famed for its fabulously fresh rhubarb, asparagus and raspberries, as well as its delightful family of farm animals including ducks, bantams and pigs. **Call 01747 829072 or visit anstypyo.co.uk. You can find your nearest farm where you can pick your own fruit or veg at pickyourownfarms.org.uk**

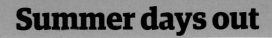

DAY TRIPPER

The influence of Liverpool's most famous sons, The Beatles, can be felt everywhere in this city of music. Fans will love International Beatleweek (call 0151 236 9091 or visit internationalbeatleweek.com) which takes over the streets in late August, complete with city-wide performances, outdoor shows and a massive Beatles marketplace. However, if you prefer to escape the crowds why not take yourself off in search of the real Penny Lane, where Paul McCartney and John Lennon used to catch the bus into town. Take a trip to Strawberry Field, another Beatles landmark which is a former Salvation Army children's home, then round off your visit at the world-famous Cavern Club which is free until 8pm on weekdays and midday at weekends.

TRY SOMETHING NEW

There's something incredibly precious about discovering the best of British countryside on horseback, whether you used to ride as a child or have never tried it before. Horse riding can be incredibly calming as well as helping you improve balance and co-ordination. **Contact your local riding centre or visit hoofride.co.uk to find out more about taking adult horse-riding lessons.**

3 OF THE BEST... SEASIDE PIERS

Nothing sums up the British seaside holiday quite like a stroll along the pier. So grab an ice-cream and explore some old-fashioned seaside fun with our pick of the best.

◆ Blackpool Central Pier has been providing entertainment to holidaymakers and locals alike since 1867, and became famous for open-air dancing during the Second World War. Today its 108ft wheel and fairground activities still make it an exciting place where you can shelter from the sun's rays and escape the crowded beach.

◆ Clevedon Pier's elegant wrought iron arches still cut a striking figure against the Somerset sea and sky. Summer here welcomes the opening of the Japanese pagoda-style café, while September sees the Waverley, the world's last sea-going paddle steamer, set off from the pier.

◆ It doesn't get much more eccentric than Southwold Pier in Suffolk where quirky end-of-the-pier-style amusements include a wacky hall of mirrors. You'll find traditional Punch and Judy shows, lovely coastal gifts and coffee and food stops, so grab a tasty treat to take to the beach!

GO BEHIND THE SCENES OF HISTORY

Love exploring the past? The National Trust offers an amazing range of working holidays for volunteers, where you can help with heritage projects and step behind the scenes in the most fascinating historic houses in Britain. As well as the chance to step behind the doors marked 'private', you'll learn how to handle historic collections, use archives and help maintain the houses that tell us so much about our history. **Call 0344 800 3099 or visit nationaltrust.org.uk/holidays/working-holidays**

Flowers of the sun

Melissa Mabbitt shows us how to bring rays of golden sunshine into ours gardens with the bright blooms of sunflowers

A golden sunflower is the epitome of the lazy, hazy days of late summer. Their brassy heads follow the late summer sun as it travels across the sky, glowing with a glorious warmth that signals the hottest season is at its peak.

In rustic tones of burnt orange, fiery reds and sunlit yellows, these flowers conjure the peaceful rural idyll wherever you live. Their tones fit in with both the super-modern and country-casual trends, especially in the sun-drenched days of August. The classic giant golden sunflower topping a towering stem is just one of the huge bunch of colourful and extravagant easy-to-grow flowers this season. Some are multi-headed, or short, or grow in delicate colours you wouldn't normally associate with a sunflower. There's one to suit every kind of garden, whatever style or size it is.

What they do need is lots of sun, at least six hours every day. Their botanical name, helianthus, literally means 'flower of the sun'. So always plant them somewhere bright and open in your garden. In front of a sunny wall or fence is an ideal spot, where the taller varieties will bring colour to the back of a flowerbed. You can put shorter plants, such as roses or daylilies, or even a few shorter varieties of sunflowers in front. Sunflowers are the perfect plant for making a bold statement in your garden, and they'll last until the summer heat starts to wane into the mellow autumn. As an added bonus, as the flowers fade, they'll turn into bronze discs covered in tiny seeds that wild birds absolutely love, so you'll be helping the wildlife in your garden, as well as adding a little sunshine to your plot.

HOW TO GROW SUNFLOWERS

If planting in June or July, buy sunflowers as small plants from a garden centre. If planting in March or April, try growing them from seed. It's super simple to do and a packet costs just a pound or two, giving you dozens of sunflowers ready to plant in your garden. To sow them, fill several small pots with compost, firm it down and push two seeds into each one, just below the surface of the compost. Water each pot until it runs out of the bottom, and leave in a sunny place until the small plants appear. Keep sprinkling on water every day, and at the end of May they'll be big enough to move outside.

To plant them in your garden, dig a small hole twice as wide as the pot but the same depth. Take the sunflower out of its pot, handling it gently so you don't snap the tall stem, and place the roots in the hole. Fill the sides of the hole with soil and firm it in, then pour water around the roots to settle it in.

Slugs and snails love to eat tender young sunflowers, so scatter a few slug pellets around the base of each, or protect them with a copper ring.

Being sun-lovers you might think sunflowers also like dry sandy soil, but in fact they need plenty of water and a nutrient-rich soil to be able to grow such big, beautiful flowers. So before you plant, add a bucket of compost to the soil and lightly dig it in. This will help the soil stay moist. Add a handful of slow-release fertiliser pellets such as Incredibloom (£4.99 vanmeuwen.com) when you plant, or water on a liquid fertiliser such as MiracleGro All Purpose concentrated liquid fertiliser (£3.97 diy.com) every two weeks.

GIVE TALL PLANTS SUPPORT

As they grow tall, whether a bought plant or grown from seed, sunflowers with large flowers will need some support. Push a cane into the soil alongside the roots and tie it to the stem, or splash out on tall and gorgeous wire plant supports, such as the elegant cones and obelisks available at crocus.co.uk.

ENJOY YEAR AFTER YEAR

Sunflowers are annual plants, meaning after they flower and fade they won't grow again, but there is one sunflower that gives you great value for money by returning year after year. Known as the perennial sunflower, Helianthus laetiflorus is tall and branching with slender waving stems and many pale yellow flowers. It forms a large clump that's best planted at the back of a flower bed and like the other types of sunflowers, it thrives in sun and rich soil.

THREE OF THE BEST FOR PRETTY PALE FLOWERS

'STARBURST LEMON ÉCLAIR'
A zesty lemon sunflower with shaggy petals. Height 150cm. £2.99/20 seeds suttons.co.uk

'ITALIAN WHITE'
Creamy white flowers with chocolate coloured centres. Height 1.2m. £2.99/40 seeds thompson-morgan.com

'JADE GREEN'
These open a limey green and fade to pale lemon white. Height 90cm. £2.99/20 seeds suttons.co.uk

Fabric flowers

These fun and summery flowers are a quick and easy way of cheering up a room...

Handy tip:
Two fat quarters will make four flowers. These versatile flowers can also be made into a corsage or attached to a hairband or hairslide.

1 Draw one 13cm (5in) circle on one fabric and one 21cm (8¼in) diameter in a different fabric. Cut out the two circles.

2 Sew a line of tacking 6mm (¼in) from the edge of the larger circle.

3 Draw up the thread to create gathers around the edge of the circle.

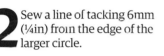

4 Pull the thread tight and tie off the ends to create a puff shape.

5 Repeat steps 2, 3 and 4 with the smaller circle.

6 With the flat side of both circles underneath, place the smaller circle on top of the larger one and sew them together in the centre.

7 Sew a button onto the centre of the flower covering up the joins.

8 Sew the stalk onto the back of the flower in the centre.

9 Repeat steps 1 to 8 until you have made a bunch of flowers.

MATERIALS:
2 fat quarters in contrasting fabrics, or 12.5x12.5cm (5x5in) and 21x21cm (8¼x8¼in) scraps for each flower
20cm x 8mm (8x5/16in) green foam ties for the stalks
1 brightly coloured small button per flower
Pencil
Drawing compass or 21cm (8¼in) diameter plate and 13cm (5¼in) diameter saucer or similar
Tape measure or ruler
Dress-making scissors
Pins
Sewing needle
Thread to match fabric

Fat Quarter: Quick Makes, by Juliet Bawden & Amanda Russell published by GMC Publications, £12.99, available from www.thegmcgroup.com

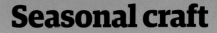

Why we love...
Autumn

Autumn heralds the transition into winter and the natural world puts on a final flurry of amazing activity before slowing down until the warmer sunshine of spring returns. At this time of year, deciduous trees and plants begin their dormancy cycle, turning the landscape into a kaleidoscope of colour as their leaves turn into rich auburns, oranges and browns before shedding to create crispy carpets everywhere. With longer nights and increased moisture in the air, there is no shortage of misty morning walks to enjoy. Take a look round any meadow, hedgerow or garden and you'll be rewarded by the sight of delicate spiders' webs outlined in dew. Explore further afield and you might be lucky enough to witness the locking of antlers and the bellowing of stags during the rutting season, while other wildlife frantically forages for the last offerings before laying low for the long winter ahead. As temperatures drop at dusk and the nights begin to draw in, the distinctive smell of bonfires and chimney smoke tinges the cool air.

FUNGI FORAYS

After the warmth of summer and dampness of autumn, woodland floors and meadows see an explosion of mushrooms and toadstools. Fungi forays are their 'fruiting bodies', preparing to release the spores from which the next generation of fungi will grow.

A SKY-HIGH SPECTACLE

The pulsating clouds of hundreds of thousands of starlings all swirling and turning in unison are known as murmurations. These fascinating displays can be sighted over fields, woodlands and reedbeds just before dusk, as they seek out their communal roosting site for the night.

RICH PICKINGS

An abundance of colours and shapes in the form of nuts, seeds and fruit are harvested by many species looking to build up their fat reserves for migration or hibernation. Firm favourites include blackberries, rose-hips, crab apples and elderberries, while acorns are often snaffled up by jays and squirrels.

PICS: ALAMY STOCK PHOTO

ATLANTIC ADVENTURES

October marks the start of the most arduous journey of an Atlantic salmon's life. After maturing at sea, it must force its way upstream, leaping barriers and negotiating rapids. Such sights can be witnessed in Scotland, Wales and in England in Yorkshire and Devon.

Autumn antics

WILD WONDERS

Watching one of Britain's few surviving wild animals, the red deer, proudly toss its antlers back and bellow into the frost, has to be one of the most magnificent sights of the season. Autumn is deer rutting time when the males roar and go into battle together to see who will get the girls! Best seen after dawn or at dusk and obviously from a safe distance, the Eastern Moors in the Peak District is a brilliant vantage point to get a front row ticket to the action. **Call 0114 289 1543 or visit visit-eastern-moors.org.uk**

FOREST FLAIR

There's no need to traipse all the way to New England to see the most amazing scenes of natural colour. Instead the UK boasts its own fair share of startling auburns, oranges, reds and browns. Feel the crunch of leaves underfoot as you take in the stunning sights of Loch Lomond which puts on the most eye-popping show come September. The Millennium Forest Trial on the west bank of the loch takes you through an avenue of oak groves into a high knoll where you'll get panoramic loch views.

IN SEARCH OF MR DARCY

Grab your bonnet for a trip to one of Britain's most refined cities, Bath. Not just home to the ancient Roman mineral baths that still provide relaxation and healing to many visitors today, Bath also bustles with museums, galleries, some of the best independent shops in the country, the iconic Royal Crescent and a packed programme of festivals, theatre and music. September usually plays host to the annual Jane Austen Festival when literary lovers dress up in their Regency costumes for talks, balls and more. **Call 01225 443000 or visit janeaustenfestivalbath.co.uk**

TO THE LIGHTHOUSE

Summer isn't the only time to go exploring Britain's coast. Leave it till later to escape the tourist crowds and swap sunbathing on the beach for a look-out for lighthouses. Full of romance and nostalgia, they stand proudly telling brave stories of how they've kept our shores and sailors safe for decades. Beachy Head Lighthouse in East Sussex is a true superstar, its quintessentially British red and white stripes having made cameos in several TV shows and films.

TRY SOMETHING NEW

Back to school time for the little ones often has us hankering after starting something new of our own. And autumn is the perfect time to get creative with a little artwork as we can put to canvas the gorgeous autumn landscapes springing up around us. If you're unsure how to get started, taking an art holiday is a great way to get going with access to a dedicated tutor, equipment and programme of learning. You'll find individual art retreats in destinations around the UK or Alpha Painting Holidays host vacation classes in a variety of locations. **Call 01934 733877 or visit alphapaintingholidays.com**

3 OF THE BEST...
CHARMING CASTLES

Circle the moat and charge through the drawbridge, step back into the myths and legends of the past and discover your inner King or Queen at the UK's most majestic castles.

◆ One of the most commanding fortresses on the English skyline, Dover Castle has been the gateway to the realm for nine centuries and with jaw-dropping sea views taking in Dover's White Cliffs, it's easy to see why it's stood here for so long. From medieval interiors to secret wartime tunnels, a visit charts many chapters of our country's fascinating history. **Call 0370 333 1181 or visit www.english-heritage.org.uk**

◆ Warwick Castle is 'joust' the ticket for a family day out filled to the turrets with fun including trebuchet-firing cannon balls, live battles and spellbinding stories of pampered princesses and heroic knights brought to life. **Call 0871 265 2000 or visit warwick-castle.com**

◆ Overlooking the sandy beaches of Northumberland and Holy Island, Bamburgh Castle in Northumberland truly has a fairytale feel. The Royal Seat of Northumbria since 1894, its imposing walls have been witness to all kinds of rebellion, myth and stories as the home to both Anglo-Saxon royals and eccentric Victorian inventors. **Call 01668 214208 or visit bamburghcastle.com**

Spires of salvias

Rainbow droplets of bright and opulent colour will add a dash of vibrancy to your garden this autumn, explains Melissa Mabbitt...

Autumn gardens have plenty of russets and golds, but if you're hankering for the brighter colours of earlier months, plant salvias to bring back the look of summer. These delicate yet colour-charged blooms have the power to paint your garden with colour, each tiny bloom like a set of pouting lips painted with tropical pink, deep Atlantic blue, creamy peach-rose or rich, velvety purple. Salvias flower from June right through to November, so they're one of the best plants for extending colour through the seasons.

They're easy to grow as long as the soil is light and sandy and they have plenty of heat. They're sun-worshippers that flourish in Mediterranean-like situations, so, if your soil tends to dry out, and you don't like to spend much time watering, you'll love salvias. The flowers form chunky spikes of tiny but thickly clustered blooms or are dotted over airy stems that make clouds of fragrant colour. Most grow up to 50-75cm, but a few will put out tall flower spikes that reach up to 1.2m. Salvias are types of sage so have the same spicy aromatic leaves as the herb.

In the garden, they can be overwhelmed by big blowsy plants such as hardy geraniums or peonies, so plant them with upright plants such as Verbena bonariensis, lavender and grasses, which will mix with them more gracefully and also enjoy the same well drained and sunny conditions. These combinations are also effortlessly modern, with beautifully bright yet stylish combinations of colour and texture.

Plant five or more salvias in flower beds at least a metre wide interspersed with grasses of the same height. The buff-coloured, softly textured grass will create the ideal backdrop for the bright but dainty flowers, allowing the salvias' colours to pop.

CHOOSE THE PERFECT ONE

There are hundreds of different garden salvias to choose from, most originating from arid and hot countries. Many are slightly tender and will be killed by a cold UK winter, so if you want your salvias to reliably come back year after year, stick to the hardiest varieties. The lavender-like Salvia nemorosa and S. sylvestris have stiff purple or blue spikes of violet flowers that last for months. Violet cold-resistant salvia 'Amistad' grows to 1.2m with spikes of deep blue flowers, while 'Crystal Blue' is a hardy variety with a softer cloudy blue colour. Cheery 'Hot Lips' has bright red and white flowers that look like they are puckering up for a kiss, while 'Day Glow' lives up to its name with luminous rose-pink blooms. And, of course, the culinary salvia, more often known as sage, is a hardy plant too, growing with grey-green, purple and cream splashed leaves and sometimes short spikes of mauve blossom.

If you find a salvia that you love that's labelled as half-hardy you can still grow it with a little extra care. If your soil is well-drained and sandy and you have a sunny spot in front of a sheltered house wall or fence, they will probably come through winter with just a covering of protective mulch. Place a 15cm thick layer of bark chips or compost around the root area and stems in late autumn, but don't cut back any of the stems as these also provide a layer of protection. If your garden is cold and windy or if the soil gets soggy in winter, grow half-hardy salvias in containers and move them into your garage or shed in the coldest months between November and March.

There are tender salvias that can be grown as annuals. They are best thrown away when the flowers fade and replaced with new plants each year. Usually called S. splendens, they have letterbox red flowers unmatched by most other summer blooms.

THREE OF THE BEST COLD-PROOF SALVIA PLANTS

'SENSATION ROSE'
Hardy, with plum-purple stems bursting into rosepink flower spikes. £13.99
thompson-morgan.com

'SCHNEEHUGEL'
A neat plant with a mass of rocketing flower spikes of white blossom. £4.95
claireaustin-hardyplants.co.uk

'BLUE MARVEL'
This new variety has larger flowers than many hardy varieties, in a deep violet-blue. £12.99
thompson-morgan.com

Autumn wreath

Celebrate the beauty of this season with a rustic but beautiful circle of foliage

1 Decide on the size of your wreath – the one pictured is 23in. (55cm) in diameter. Gather together as many lengths of grapevine as you think you need and start shaping them into a wreath, attaching the lengths by twisting with florist's wire. The more you have the thicker it will be.

2 Start by attaching bunches of rosehips and blackberry branches first. Make a bundle of each, securing the bundle with wire, and then attach each bundle to the grapevine.

3 Add the hydrangea blooms, acorns, and oak leaves with wire to fill out the bottom half of the wreath. We like to leave the top half of the wreath free of any decoration.

4 Finally, cut a length of linen fabric to be tied in a bow at the top of the wreath. We find that the linen hangs beautifully and adds a sophisticated elegance to a rustic wreath.

MATERIALS:
Grapevine
Florist's wire
Rosehips
Blackberry branches
(the berries can be green, red, or black)
Hydrangeas
Fallen oak leaves (with acorns attached)
Linen fabric

TOOLS:
Secateurs
Scissors

Seasonal Scandi Crafts by Christiane Bellstedt Myers, published by CICO Books (£12.99) Photography by Caroline Arber © CICO Books

Why we love...
Winter

Winter is a truly magical time of year. While the nights are long and the days are short, there's no better time to sit beside a crackling fire, enjoy hearty foods and take brisk walks through the frost-capped countryside or brave the blustery coast to blow away the cobwebs. The last of the bright red berries can be seen clinging to the branches of plants and trees, adding a splash of colour to the silvery landscape before being stripped away by foraging thrushes. In the lead up to Christmas, the air is full of festive cheer, with markets popping up across the country offering copious amounts of roasted chestnuts and mulled wine, among other seasonal treats. Falling temperatures provide the perfect excuse to layer up in our favourite woollies and knit some new creations of our own too. A quick flurry of snow can see the landscape transform into a white winter wonderland, with families building snowmen and sledging down hills.

LET THERE BE LIGHT

As the nights draw in festivals are shining a new light on outdoor spaces, from woodlands to city streets and even zoos. With trails featuring laser gardens, light tunnels and even lanterns in the shape of mythical creatures, there's plenty to brighten up dark winter nights across the UK.

WINTER'S BLANKET

After the darkness of winter, snowdrops are a welcome and early sign that spring is in sight. They provide a striking bloom in the winter months when little else is growing in the British countryside, appearing between November and March and typically thriving in lightly shaded woodland areas.

CELESTIAL SHOWERS

Winter's long hours of darkness offer stargazers the opportunity to study the skies above. Early January is the time of the annual Quadrantid meteor shower - made up from debris of an asteroid, which can be witnessed in the northern skies between midnight and 2am.

PICS: ALAMY STOCK PHOTO

A SMALL FLAME

No other bird invokes the spirit of winter and the festive season like the plucky robin, whose iconic redbreast can easily be spotted against a grey wintery backdrop. They are one of a few bird species that hold their territory all year round, being mostly sedentary.

Winter wonderland

WHEN YOU WISH UPON A STAR

Wrap up warm, pack a flask of tea and discover the beauty of the night sky with a spot of stargazing. There are 17 Dark Sky Discovery Sites in the UK which are proven hotspots for catching a meteor shower or picking out the Milky Way and many hold regular stargazing events. **Visit nationalparks.uk/visiting/ outdoor-activities/dark-skies to find your nearest.**

Northumberland national park is a stellar spot for the best chance to see a whole host of wonders from the Andromeda Galaxy to a glimpse of the Northern Lights. **Call 01434 605555 or visit northumberlandnationalpark. org.uk. Stargazing is best done before the moon is full and mobile apps such as Star Walk (iPhone) or Google Sky (Android) can help tell you which stars you can see from your location.**

GO SEAL SPOTTING

The Donna Nook nature reserve in Lincolnshire puts on the most adorable winter show as a colony of thousands of grey Atlantic seals deliver their gorgeous little pups in the dunes. From November to December a special viewing platform is put in place so you can catch a glimpse of the newborns from a non-intrusive distance. **Call 01507 526667 or visit lincstrust.org.uk**

Did you know? November and December are the best time to catch the mesmerising aerial acrobatics of starlings swooping and diving in unison - called murmuration. The best place to see this hypnotising display is on the Somerset Levels.

A TASTE OF THE MED

You don't have to get on a plane to discover the joy of the Mediterranean. The Welsh tourist village of Portmeirion was totally inspired by the colours and feel of the Med and is perfect for brightening up a grey, winter's day. Once a popular haunt of The Beatles, here warm dry winds blow down the nearby mountains, making it often unseasonably mild and home to an array of exquisite exotic plants in the sub-tropical gardens.

3 OF THE BEST... WONDERFUL WATERFALLS

Enjoy one of natural Britain's most impressive performances as the winter rain backs up to produce breath-taking cascades around the country.

◆ The Brecon Beacons harbour many natural gems but one of its most sparkling jewels has to be Henrhyd Falls, the tallest waterfall in south Wales. It's well worth the journey through the wooded gorge to find this astonishing cascade that you can, with some care, walk behind when the rocks aren't too slippy.

◆ Prepare to feel like you've stepped into the pages of a children's story as you look upon magical St Nectan's Glen near Tintagel in Cornwall. Made up of a series of waterfalls, the most eye-popping is the 60ft Nectan's Kieve which is considered sacred to some, meaning the rocks are usually lined with ribbons, crystals and prayers.

◆ Hardraw Force in the Yorkshire Dales is not only England's highest single drop waterfall with a reputed drop of 100ft. It's also set within the grounds of a pub meaning you have to go through the Green Dragon - with or without grabbing some refreshments - to see it. Movie fans may also recognise the waterfall from Robin Hood, Prince of Thieves, as this was the waterfall where Maid Marion spots Robin bathing.

FLICKS IN THE STICKS

Movie fans will love being taken back to the golden age of film at the Kinema in the Woods in Woodhall Spa, Lincolnshire. Dating back to 1922, this cute-as-a-button vintage cinema is the only place in the country still using rear projection, where the latest films are projected from behind the screen and onto a mirror to flip the image. During the Second World War this place became affectionately known as 'Flicks in the Sticks' as it entertained the servicemen and women. A big treat today is watching the cinema's organ rise from under the stage at film intervals. **Call 01526 352166 or visit www.thekinemainthewoods.co.uk**

CHRISTMAS WITH CLASS

Fairytale festivities don't get much better than a seasonal trip to one of Britain's stately homes where the halls are decked with boughs of holly and other beautiful trimmings at this time of year. Castle Howard near York (01653 648333/castlehoward.co.uk), which was once the film set for Brideshead Revisited, is always especially magical, themed with a different story or setting every Christmas with an accompanying market of treats. Its sprawling grounds and iconic fountains also make for the perfect wintery walk to burn off some festive over-indulgence.

Blazing berries

Melissa Mabbitt shows us how to add fire to our winter gardens by planting the colourful and super-useful shrub pyracantha

We love plants that brighten up your garden all year round with very little effort, and pyracantha certainly tick that box. They're easy to grow in all types of soil, in sun or shade, and have something that draws your eye at almost every time of year, whether that's their creamy spring blossom or the dense clusters of fiery orange, red or yellow bead-like berries that smother the branches in autumn and winter.

Also known as firethorn, these shrubs can be grown against a wall to show off their neat, branching shape. In winter, their evergreen leaves are useful for creating structure when the rest of the garden is bare. In the summer months, while the berries are slowly developing, the glossy green leaves make a useful backdrop for showy flowers.

The long thorns that hide beneath the leaves make them ideal for growing into a secure hedge and as they don't take up much space, they're perfect for small gardens. In almost every way, they have a useful quality that makes them well worth growing.

HOW TO GROW

Pyracantha bushes will grow in any soil apart from very boggy ground. They thrive in sun or shade, though they will produce more berries if they have a few hours of sunshine every day. You can plant them at any time of year so long as the ground isn't frozen. November is the perfect time to plant pyracantha, as the soil is still relatively warm, which will give the roots a head start. Though they are tough plants, they will reward you with lots of healthy growth if you give them a little extra care.

Make sure the main stem isn't planted too low in the ground, which can cause rotting. Don't make the planting hole much deeper than the pot, but make it approximately twice as wide. Use the original compost level of the pot as a guide, aiming to keep the top of the compost level with the surrounding soil once planted. Fill the sides of the hole with soil and firm it down with your hands. If it's a tall shrub, pushing a cane into the ground next to it can help keep it stable. Wear thick gloves to handle the stems to avoid getting pricked by the thorns.

Add a handful of slow-release fertiliser pellets to the ground when you plant them. Pour on a full can of water weekly between May and September in their first growing season after being planted. In winter or spring, pile on a handspan-thick layer of compost over the soil around the roots, which will help to keep them healthy.

KEEP THEM IN CONTAINERS

Their naturally upright shape makes pyracantha easy to accommodate in a pot, where they will look good grouped with other autumn plants such as grasses or amber-tinted heuchera. Pyracantha varieties such as 'Red Column' have a particularly neat outline that makes them good for container growing. Choose a pot that's at least 40cm (15½in) wide and deep. They will need repotting every two years into a slightly larger container to keep them thriving. Once they are in a pot that's as big as you can accommodate, you can just remove any other plants, scrape off the top few centimetres of compost every spring, sprinkle some slow-release fertiliser pellets on the surface then cover with a new layer of fresh compost and any other plants you want. Just remember to water them regularly if they're in a pot. Twice weekly with a full can of water from April to October should be enough.

THREE OF THE BEST FOR STUNNING COLOUR

'SAPHYR JAUNE'
A pale yellow-berried pyracantha perfect for growing as a hedge or against a wall. £17.99 crocus.co.uk

'MOHAVE'
An upright variety covered in red berries that makes an ideal hedge. £9.99 mailordertrees.co.uk

'ORANGE GLOW'
The tangerine orange of the berries will add zing to your garden. £4.59 best4hedging.co.uk

Pom-pom pudding

An iconic symbol of a traditional Christmas, this cute little pudding bauble is quick and fun to make...

Materials and tools:

Oddments of black, brown, muddy green, beige and white DK yarns
6.5cm (2½in) pom-pom maker
Green embroidery thread and needle
Small scraps of green felt
Small, sharp scissors
Knitting needle (or similar blunt tool)
3 x small red bells

Seasonal craft

1 Wrap and fill one half of your pom-pom maker with an assortment of yarn. Use five colours together such as one black, two brown, one muddy green and one beige. This will create the speckled bottom half of your pudding.

2 Wrap and fill the other half of your pom-pom maker with white yarn to create the topping. Close, cut and tie the pom-pom with a length of white yarn before releasing it from the pom-pom maker. Give it a good, hard trim with small, sharp scissors, retaining the white tie yarn tails.

LEAF TEMPLATES

3 Use the end of the knitting needle (and your fingers) to push and manipulate the line where your speckled pudding base meets the white top. This should create a wavy edge where the two contrasting halves join.

4 Cut two small leaves from the green felt scraps using the templates below. Thread your needle with green embroidery thread. Push the needle up through your pom-pom from the centre of the bottom of the speckled half and out through the top of the white half – leaving a tail at the bottom to secure later. Feed your needle tip firstly through the base of one leaf, then the loop on each of the three little bells and, finally, through the base of the second leaf.

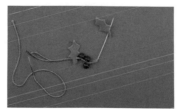

5 Push the needle back down through the pom-pom from the top to the bottom, drawing it through carefully, but firmly, to secure the leaves and bells snugly into place at the top of the bauble.

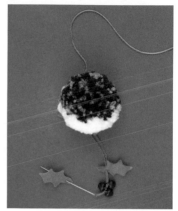

6 Tie the two ends of the green embroidery thread firmly together and trim them so that the ends are lost in the pile of the speckled pom-pom yarn. Finally, tie the two white yarn ends together and trim neatly to create your hanging loop.

A Very Pompom Christmas, by Jemima Schlee published by GMC Publications, £9.99 available from www.thegmcgroup.com

Notable dates 2020

New Year's Day (Bank Holiday observed)	Wednesday January 1
Bank Holiday (Scotland)	Thursday January 2
Epiphany	Monday January 6
Burn's Night	Saturday January 25
Chinese New Year (Rat)	Saturday January 25
Shrove Tuesday (Pancake Day)	Tuesday February 25
Valentine's Day	Friday February 14
Ash Wednesday	Wednesday February 26
St David's Day	Sunday March 1
Commonwealth Day	Monday March 9
St Patrick's Day (Bank Holiday N. Ireland/Eire)	Tuesday March 17
Mothering Sunday	Sunday March 22
British Summer Time begins (clocks go forward)	Sunday March 29
Palm Sunday	Sunday April 5
First Day of Passover (Jewish Holiday)	Wednesday April 8
Maundy Thursday	Thursday April 9
Good Friday (Bank Holiday)	Friday April 10
Easter Sunday	Sunday April 12
Easter Monday (Bank Holiday)	Monday April 13
First Day of Ramadan (Islam)	Thursday April 23
St George's Day	Thursday April 23
May Bank Holiday (VE Day 75 years anniversary)	Friday May 8
Ascension Day	Thursday May 21
Spring Bank Holiday	Monday May 25
Summer Solstice (Longest day)	Saturday June 20
Father's Day	Sunday June 21
Armed Forces Day	Saturday June 27
American Independence Day	Saturday July 4
Battle of the Boyne (Holiday N. Ireland)	Sunday July 12
St Swithin's Day	Wednesday July 15
Summer Bank Holiday (Scotland / Eire)	Monday August 3
Islamic New Year	Wednesday August 19
Summer Bank Holiday	Monday August 31
Jewish New Year (Rosh Hashanah)	Friday September 18
Trafalgar Day	Wednesday October 21
British Summer Time ends (clocks go back)	Sunday October 25
Hallowe'en	Saturday October 31
All Saints' Day	Sunday November 1
Guy Fawkes' Night	Thursday November 5
Remembrance Sunday	Sunday November 8
Diwali (Hindu Festival)	Saturday November 14
First Sunday in Advent	Sunday November 29
St Andrew's Day	Monday November 30
Winter Solstice (Shortest day)	Monday December 21
Christmas Day	Friday December 25
Boxing Day	Saturday December 26
New Year's Eve/Hogmanay	Thursday December 31

THE YEAR AHEAD

29 SUNDAY

30 MONDAY

31 TUESDAY

1 WEDNESDAY

2 THURSDAY

3 FRIDAY

4 SATURDAY

A magical memory

SNOWY SNOWDON WALK

I have lived in North Wales nearly all of my life and have climbed most of its hills apart from Crib Goch. This photo was taken of me halfway up Snowdon one winter. One of the most straightforward walks is from Llanberis by the Snowdon Mountain railway station. I have only ever been up the mountain once on the train. It was a beautiful sunny day and I thoroughly enjoyed it. There was just enough time to get a coffee and cake at the café before it was time to take the train back down.

Once I was caught in mist on top of a mountain with some other people. We found our way down again with the aid of a compass – the only time I've used a compass in years of hill walking. Sometimes I'd find the uphill walk a struggle but the panoramic views on reaching the summit were splendid. These days I have to stick to the lower hills such as the Little Orme and Great Orme in Llandudno and Conwy Mountain.

Linda Nesbitt, Colwyn Bay

On this week

JANUARY 3, 1987: **The Rock & Roll Hall of Fame welcomed the first ever female artist into its hallowed halls as Aretha Franklin joins the likes of Buddy Holly, Elvis Presley and James Brown recognised for their contribution to music.**

In the garden
Watch the birdie

As we welcome in the new year and move further into the freezing cold winter, make sure any flying friends have a safe spot to rest. Create a safe haven in your garden by popping a bird box 2-4m up in a sheltered, shaded area of your garden and fill it with twigs and grass cuttings to keep them warm.

I never knew that!

The deepest snow ever recorded in the UK came after the heavy winter of 1946-47. In March 1947, a snow depth of 1.65m was recorded near Ruthin, in North Wales. That winter saw freezing temperatures from January to March followed by severe flooding.

Wonderful wildlife on your doorstep!

PIC: ALAMY STOCK PHOTO

NAME: **Fox**

HABITAT: **Common throughout the UK in rural and urban areas.**

DIET: **Scavengers by nature, foxes will eat insects, earthworms, fruit, berries, plus small mammals and birds.**

FAST FACT: **Although related to dogs, foxes are very like cats. They stalk their prey and are the only member of the dog family that can climb trees.**

Recipe of the week

EVE'S PUDDING

SERVES: 4 PREP: 10 MINS COOK: 35 MINS

400g (14oz) Braeburn apples, cored and diced
100g (4oz) butter, softened
100g (4oz) caster sugar
2 eggs
100g (4oz) self-raising flour

1 Preheat the oven to 180°C/350°F/Gas Mark 4. Place the apple pieces in a saucepan with 50ml (2fl oz) water. Cook covered for 3-4 mins. Transfer to a shallow ovenproof dish.
2 Meanwhile, beat the butter and sugar together until pale and fluffy. Whisk in the eggs one at a time, then gradually fold in the flour.
3 Spoon the mixture over the apples and bake for 30-35 mins until golden and cooked throughout. Serve with custard.
www.waitrose.com/recipes

5 SUNDAY

6 MONDAY

7 TUESDAY

8 WEDNESDAY

9 THURSDAY

10 FRIDAY

11 SATURDAY

A magical memory

A DUET WITH DAVE

Back in the Fifties there was no X Factor on television for wannabe singers like me, but as I was a great fan of the actor and singer Dave King I wrote to The Daily Mirror's 'Junior Mirror Wish Corner' saying that I would love to meet and sing with my hero. After sending dozens of begging letters, I was lucky enough to be chosen.

On the day, I was taken with a newspaper reporter backstage to the dressing room at the theatre where Dave King was performing. When I explained that I had always dreamed of being a singer he said: "Come on then, let's go!" He got some music and sang the first note, then we sang the song together. He was the kindest person you could wish to meet and made sure our meeting would be one to remember for the rest of my life.

Many years later, my husband and I went to see him at the Marlowe theatre in Canterbury. We arranged to meet him afterwards and went for a drink at his hotel. What a lovely man!
Maureen Andrews, via email

On this week

JANUARY 11, 1973: **The first-ever graduates of the Open University were awarded their degrees after two years of studying at home. Out of the 1,000 students that sat the final exams, 867 graduated, kickstarting one of the most successful adult learning programmes ever.**

In the garden

Recycle your Christmas tree

The time has come to take down the Christmas decorations. Did you know that real Christmas trees make perfect garden mulch? Start by removing the branches and needles which can decompose slowly. You can make all sorts out of the trunk by sawing it into coasters or even logs for the fire.

I never knew that!

Queen Victoria and Prince Albert were given a huge block of cheese as a wedding present in 1840. The cheese wheel had a diameter of around nine feet and was made from the milk of 750 cows! After the wedding it was sent off to be exhibited by local farmers and the Queen declined to have the cheese returned!

Wonderful wildlife on your doorstep!

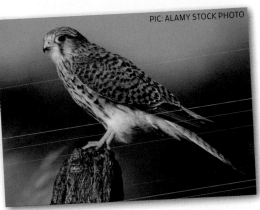

PIC: ALAMY STOCK PHOTO

NAME: **Kestrel**

HABITAT: **Across the UK in countryside and urban areas, although it prefers grass and farm land.**

DIET: **Small mammals, particularly field voles, mice and small birds.**

FAST FACT: **The kestrel was given the nickname windhover because of its ability to be able to keep its head still while hovering to search for prey.**

Recipe of the week

MEXICAN-STYLE EGGS

SERVES: 4 PREP: 2 MINS COOK: 10 MINS

1 tbsp oil
1 bunch spring onions, sliced
1 tbsp chipotle paste
400g (14oz) can chopped tomatoes
400g (14oz) can red kidney beans, drained and rinsed
4 free-range eggs
28g (1oz) fresh coriander, chopped
Tortilla crisps, to serve (optional)

1 Heat the oil in a frying pan and fry the spring onions for 2 mins. Stir in the chipotle paste, add the tomatoes and beans and cook gently for 3-4 mins.
2 Make 4 wells in the mixture and crack an egg into each one. Cook for 2 mins then place under a preheated grill for 2 mins or until the eggs are cooked to your liking.
3 Sprinkle with coriander and a few tortilla crisps if desired.
www.waitrose.com/recipes

12 SUNDAY

13 MONDAY

14 TUESDAY

15 WEDNESDAY

16 THURSDAY

17 FRIDAY

18 SATURDAY

A magical memory

UP ON THE ROOF

This is the view from the roof of my old home in Greyhound Road, Tottenham. At the front there were railings to stop you toppling over on to the pavement below. My sister and I used to take water pistols up there and shoot them at people walking past. Great fun for us kids! There were no railings at the back and we used to sit on the wall with our legs dangling above the garden. I'd be too scared to do that now.

Our friend Beryl would lie on the roof with us and we'd make out shapes in the clouds. We called ourselves cloudologists. At night, when the sky was clear, we'd go up there with our dad who would point out the different stars and constellations. The streets were quite dark as they were lit by gaslight so the stars were visible.

From our roof you could see the BBC mast at Alexandra Palace and when Spurs had a home match you could hear the roar of the crowd when a goal was scored. Such happy memories!
Valerie Temple, Great Dunmow

On this week

JANUARY 17, 1983: **This morning the nation got up extra early to watch Britain's first-ever breakfast news programme, BBC Breakfast Time, presented by Frank Bough and Selina Scott. TV-am's Good Morning Britain launched just two weeks later, starting an immediate ratings battle.**

In the garden

January blues

Add some much-needed colour to your garden during this gloomy winter period by planting some bright and beautiful sweet violet. These lavender-blue flowers give off a lovely sweet scent and will continue to flower and bring joy through to early summer.

I never knew that!

Elizabeth Taylor had such a bond with her equine co-star Pie in the 1944 film National Velvet, that after filming he was given to her as a gift. The chestnut thoroughbred stallion called King Charles was reportedly a tricky character and would bite the cast and crew, but was always nice as pie with Taylor!

Wonderful wildlife on your doorstep!

PIC: ALAMY STOCK PHOTO

NAME: **Grass snake**
HABITAT: **Widespread across England and Wales in wetlands, grasslands and gardens.**
DIET: **Small mammals, birds, amphibians and toads.**
FAST FACT: **The UK's largest snake is an expert at playing dead when threatened! Adult snakes will lie still, loll their tongues and even roll their eyes in a convincing act!**

Recipe of the week

ORECCHIETTE PASTA WITH BROCCOLI AND PRAWNS

SERVES: 4 PREP: 5 MINS COOK: 10 MINS

400g (14oz) dried orecchiette pasta
200g (7oz) tenderstem broccoli
Large knob of butter
400g (14oz) raw peeled prawns
3 cloves of garlic, crushed
Pinch of dried chilli flakes
Handful of flat-leaf parsley

1 Cook the orecchiette pasta according to the packet instructions.
2 Cut the broccoli florets, slicing the stem, then steam or boil for about 3 mins until just tender.
3 Sauté the prawns in butter with the garlic and chilli flakes until the prawns are pink and just cooked through.
4 Add the chopped parsley and season.
5 Add the cooked pasta and broccoli to the prawns, toss well and serve immediately.
www.tenderstem.co.uk

19 SUNDAY

20 MONDAY

21 TUESDAY

22 WEDNESDAY

23 THURSDAY

24 FRIDAY

25 SATURDAY

A magical memory

AN ALPINE ADVENTURE

I had never been abroad before I retired so when one of my cousins rang and asked if I would like to go to Austria with her the following February, I accepted even though I didn't have a passport at that time.

As I have never been particularly fond of boats, I was wary of going on the ferry from Dover to Calais, but we had a calm crossing. We travelled by coach to our hotel which was in a lovely little village called Brandenberg. It was a good job we arrived in the dark as the next morning we discovered there was a mountain on one side of us and on the other side of the road was a valley so steep you couldn't even see the bottom. Among the highlights of our holiday were a visit to Salzburg, a trip by steam train to Mayrhofen and a horse and carriage ride through the woods in Kitzbuhel.

I thoroughly enjoyed the whole holiday but especially the day when we borrowed two sledges and had a great time sliding around in the snow in the field behind our hotel.

Margaret Leonard, Warrington

On this week

JANUARY 24, 1961: **Hollywood siren Marilyn Monroe announced her divorce from playwright husband Arthur Miller. It came after years of quarrels and shortly after finishing their latest film together, The Misfits, where the pair reportedly barely spoke to each other on set.**

In the garden

Stop the freeze

If you have a pond or a bird feeder in your garden, you'll want to avoid it freezing over. Try popping a tennis ball on top to stop the water becoming impenetrable. This will allow feathered visitors, who are easily dehydrated in frosty weather, to quench their thirst while keeping your pond in motion.

I never knew that!

Chanel's iconic first fragrance was named simply because Coco Chanel preferred the fifth sample presented to her by perfumier Ernest Beaux, making Chanel No.5 a fitting choice. The scent was developed with the modern woman in mind and of course it was the only thing Marilyn Monroe wore to bed.

Wonderful wildlife on your doorstep!

PIC: ALAMY STOCK PHOTO

NAME: **Water vole**
HABITAT: **Grassy banks of rivers, streams, ditches and wet moorland across the UK.**
DIET: **Grasses, tree bark, reeds and fruit.**
FAST FACT: **Ratty from Wind in the Willows was a water vole and not a rat. Sadly, the water vole population has decreased rapidly over recent years.**

Recipe of the week

BEEF AND GREEN BEAN NOODLE SALAD

SERVES: 3-4 PREP: 10 MINS COOK: 5 MINS

200g (7oz) fine green beans, trimmed
Juice 1 lime
2 tbsp sweet chilli sauce
250g (9oz) pack beef frying steak
1 tsp sunflower oil
1 tbsp Thai red curry paste
300g (10½ oz) pack fresh egg noodles
2 little gem lettuces, shredded
1 small red onion, very thinly sliced
2 tbsp basil or coriander leaves, chopped

1 Cook the beans in a large pan of boiling water for 2 mins until tender. Drain, then cool under running water.
2 Stir together the lime juice and sweet chilli sauce to make the dressing.
3 Mix together the steak, oil and curry paste until the meat is evenly coated. Heat a wok or large frying pan and stir-fry the steak over a high heat for 3 mins until nicely browned.
4 Toss together the cooked beans, noodles, lettuce, red onion and sweet chilli dressing. Stir through the cooked steak and scatter with herbs before serving.

www.waitrose.com/recipes

26 SUNDAY

27 MONDAY

28 TUESDAY

29 WEDNESDAY

30 THURSDAY

31 FRIDAY

1 SATURDAY

A magical memory

A RAILWAY CHILD

This is my grandfather (on the left) with his son, Ormie. He lived in Brynmawr, Gwent, in a little two-bedroom house with a toilet at the bottom of the garden. He had nine children and worked hard to support them, supplementing his pay as a signalman on the railway by selling daily papers in the town square.

Just as his children had all left home and he might have enjoyed some peace and quiet, he opened his doors to his London grandchildren needing refuge from the bombing during the Blitz. My mother came with me and my two sisters along with the little girl from next door and several cousins. There were a lot of us and we slept four to a bed, head to toe. I was indignant that my cousin Ray kept his socks on in bed.

I felt very special as I was the only one Granddad took to his signal box, carrying me up the steps and lifting me up to help him pull the shining levers. There were fewer health and safety rules back then!
Barbara Ketteridge, London

On this week

FEBRUARY 1, 1984: **Chancellor of the Exchequer Nigel Lawson announced that the halfpenny coin was to meet its maker, leaving the nation's purses after 13 years of almost universal unpopularity thanks to its fiddly size and poor worth, equivalent to just 1.2 pre-decimal pence.**

In the garden

Split your snowdrops

You'll find that the little white flowers will be popping up all over to cheer us up in these dark months. Buy and plant your bulbs throughout February and March and once they have finished flowering, dig up and separate the mass of flowers, ensuring the bulbs remain intact before replanting them all over your garden.

I never knew that!

A single walking step uses 200 muscles making it a great and easy way to workout – that's also joint-friendly. Walk daily at a brisk pace and you could see lots of health benefits, including improved heart health and circulation, plus lower blood pressure.

Wonderful wildlife on your doorstep!

PIC: ALAMY STOCK PHOTO

NAME: **Mole**
HABITAT: **Widespread across the UK, in grasslands, woodland and gardens.**
DIET: **Earthworms and insect larvae.**
FAST FACT: **Moles are amazing diggers and will easily tunnel up to 20 metres a day, digging out large chambers on the surface and also deep underground.**

Recipe of the week

POACHED EGG AND KALE MUFFINS

SERVES: 1 PREP: 4 MINS COOK: 10 MINS

1 courgette, sliced lengthways
50g (2oz) kale
2 medium eggs
1 wholewheat muffin, halved and toasted
1 tbsp soft cheese
1 tbsp garlic mayonnaise

1 Brush the courgette slices with a little oil and griddle for 4-5 mins turning once until softened. Meanwhile, cook the kale in boiling water for 5 mins and drain well.
2 Poach the eggs in a saucepan of boiling water to your liking.
3 Spread the muffin with the soft cheese, top with the kale and courgettes then the eggs. Spoon over the mayo, season and serve.
www.waitrose.com/recipes

2 SUNDAY

3 MONDAY

4 TUESDAY

5 WEDNESDAY

6 THURSDAY

7 FRIDAY

8 SATURDAY

A magical memory

A LOVELY, GENTLE MAN

This photo, taken when I got engaged to my first husband on my twenty-first birthday, is very precious to me. Eric was my first boyfriend and as soon as we started dating we knew we had something special. After a few months, he proposed to me in his mum and dad's front room. My parents organised a party for us in our local pub, The Folkestone Hotel. All our friends and family came and we had a fantastic night of music and dancing.

We were married in October 1968 and the following year I became pregnant. Our baby was due in March 1970 and we were both looking forward to becoming parents for the first time. However, that was not to be as Eric, aged twenty-two, died in February after a short illness of nine days. Four weeks later I gave birth to a healthy baby boy who I called Andrew Eric. His dad was a lovely, gentle man. We had only a short marriage, but I loved him very much.
Marjorie Spellman, Ashton-under-Lyne

On this week

FEBRUARY 5, 1953: **School children all over the country emptied out their piggybanks and raced for the nearest newsagents after sweet rationing finally comes to an end. After many straitened years, toffee apples, followed by sticks of nougat and liquorice strips were the confectionary to fly off the shelves the fastest.**

In the garden

Fight the frost

Before the sun goes down and the frost sets in, cover up the areas of your garden you are concerned about with a frost cloth. Prop the sheet up with sticks so that the sheet doesn't touch the plant but protects it from the soil level upwards. Remove it the next day once the frost has thawed and your plants should have been protected.

I never knew that!

The letter E is the most common letter in the English alphabet, but more English words begin with S than with any other letter. The only word in the English language with five consecutive vowels is queuing and the only two words ending with 'gry' are hungry and angry!

Wonderful wildlife on your doorstep!

PIC: ALAMY STOCK PHOTO

NAME: **Natterjack toad**

HABITAT: **Coastal areas, sand dunes, sand-grazing marshes and sandy heaths.**

DIET: **Insects and arachnids including beetles, slugs, worms and even small mice!**

FAST FACT: **The female natterjack toad can lay up to 7,500 eggs during breeding season, but are sadly still considered endangered.**

Recipe of the week

CLASSIC WATERCRESS SOUP

SERVES: 4 PREP: 5 MINS COOK: 15 MINS

1 tbsp olive oil
1 small onion, chopped
1 small stick celery
350g (12oz) potato, peeled and diced
600ml (1pt) vegetable stock
3x 85g (3oz) bags watercress
150ml (¼pt) milk
Pinch of nutmeg
Squeeze of lemon juice
Salt and freshly ground black pepper

1 Heat the oil in a large pan, add the onion and celery and sauté over a medium heat for 5 mins until pale golden.
2 Stir in the potato and stock and bring to the boil. Cover and simmer for 10 mins or until the potato is tender.
3 Stir in the watercress, cover and cook for a further 5 mins or until the watercress is wilted.
4 Transfer the soup to a food processor and blitz until smooth. Return the soup to the rinsed out pan add the milk, nutmeg, lemon juice and seasoning to taste. Gently reheat until piping hot and serve with crusty bread.
www.watercress.co.uk

9 SUNDAY

10 MONDAY

11 TUESDAY

12 WEDNESDAY

13 THURSDAY

14 FRIDAY

15 SATURDAY

A magical memory

MY FIRST VALENTINE

My dad, who played the trumpet in a band, took me to my very first dance when I was fourteen. I had no idea how I should behave so I sat frozen to my chair. The lights dimmed and the first dance, a waltz, was announced.

A young man came across and said: "My mate wants to know if he can have this dance". I said: "Tell him to ask me himself". He went back to the group of boys and one of them came over, smiled, and held out his hand. I had no idea if I could dance, but to my amazement we glided around the floor.

He sent me my first Valentine card that year and another the next year. Then came the awful news that he was called up to do his National Service. He said: "Will you write to me? I've got this strange feeling that one day I'm going to marry you." I wrote to him every single week. When I was twenty, he asked me to marry him with another Valentine card. We have been married for nearly 70 years and I still have all three Valentine cards.
Eileen Newman, Chesterfield

On this week

FEBRUARY 11, 1976: **John Curry figure skated to Britain's first Olympic gold in the sport – and the country's first medal at the winter games for 12 years. Curry wowed the judges with three immaculate triple jumps and artistic interpretation that scored him a sea of 5.9s.**

In the garden

Valentine's roses

Nothing says 'I love you' like a bunch of roses. If you're wanting some bunches around the home this Valentine's week. Place them immediately into water and remove any foliage before adding flower food or even some bleach to the vase to keep your flowers looking fresh for the Valentine's period.

I never knew that!

A dozen red roses says 'I love you' on Valentine's Day without too much of a dent in the bank balance, but the Juliet Rose is by far the most expensive rose ever created. The exquisite peach bloom reportedly cost its creator David Austin £3 million and took 15 years to create. It was showcased at the Chelsea Flower show in 2006.

Wonderful wildlife on your doorstep!

NAME: **Pine marten**

HABITAT: **Woodland mostly in Scotland and Ireland - rarely in England.**

PIC: ALAMY STOCK PHOTO

DIET: **Birds, insects and small mammals, eggs, fungi and berries.**

FAST FACT: **Like some other mammals, pine martens have the ability to delay implantation, which means they mate in summer, but their young won't be born until the following spring.**

Recipe of the week

SALMON & MINT FISHCAKES WITH DILL DIP

SERVES: 4 PREP: 15 MINS COOK: 15 MINS

700g (1lb 8oz) King Edward potatoes, diced
300g (10½oz) salmon fillets
2 medium eggs
1 bunch spring onions, thinly sliced
20g (¾oz) fresh dill, chopped
1 tbsp fresh mint, chopped
200ml (7fl oz) tub half-fat crème fraîche
2 tbsp garlic mayonnaise
1 tbsp oil

1 Cook the potatoes in boiling water for 10 mins until tender, drain and allow to cool.
2 Meanwhile, poach the salmon and eggs in boiling water for 10 mins then cool. Flake the salmon and chop the boiled eggs.
3 Mash the potato and stir in the salmon, egg, spring onions, half the dill and mint, season. Mould into 8 fishcakes and chill for 30 mins.
4 Meanwhile, mix the crème fraîche, mayo and remaining dill together and set aside.
5 Heat the oil in a pan and fry the fishcakes in 2 batches for 3-4 mins each side. Serve with the dill dip and a green salad.
www.lovefreshherbs.co.uk

16 SUNDAY	
17 MONDAY	
18 TUESDAY	
19 WEDNESDAY	
20 THURSDAY	
21 FRIDAY	
22 SATURDAY	

A magical memory

SINGAPORE DAYS

My husband was in the RAF and when he was stationed in Singapore we had an amah called Helimah who washed and ironed for us. She didn't speak much English but we managed very well with our own special sign language.

Helimah had six daughters and used to bring the eldest one, Ruguya, with her when she came to babysit for our son, David. They loved children and would bring him sweets and generally spoil him. They would also tuck him up in bed beneath two or three blankets until I persuaded them that David wasn't used to the tropical heat and didn't need any blankets. He loved helping Helimah, especially when she filled the bath with water and threw the clothes in to rinse them and he would jumped into the bath, fully clothed.

The day came when Helimah told us she was leaving to live with her family in Malaya. I told her I would like to photograph them all before they left. When I turned up at their house, the family all came out in their best clothes for the picture.

Joan Arnold, Ramsgate

On this week

FEBRUARY 18, 1969: **Our hearts went boom-bang-a-bang to see singer Lulu tie the knot with Bee Gee Maurice Gibb at a Buckinghamshire church. The bride wore white – a long, mink-trimmed coat with a fur hood as thousands of onlookers cheered them on.**

In the garden

Staying indoors

If it's a bit too chilly to get out and about in your garden this week, why not turn your attention to your houseplants? Make sure they're in a warm place to soak up plenty of sunlight. To avoid overwatering, poke your finger into the soil - if it feels damp don't water it. When you do water it, use room temperature water to benefit the roots and growth.

I never knew that!

Big Ben is not actually the name of the landmark tower in London, but the name for the bell inside it. Formerly called the Clock Tower, it was renamed the Elizabeth Tower in honour of the Queen's Diamond Jubilee in 2012.

Wonderful wildlife on your doorstep!

PIC: ALAMY STOCK PHOTO

NAME: **Exmoor pony**
HABITAT: **The open grasslands of Exmoor.**
DIET: **Grass, heather, rushes and gorse.**
FAST FACT: **At the end of the Second World War there were only around 50 registered Exmoor ponies left on the moor and today it's classed as an endangered native breed.**

Recipe of the week

THAI POTATO NOODLE BROTH WITH BASIL & LEMONGRASS

SERVES: 4 PREP: 10 MINS COOK: 10 MINS

800ml (1½ pt) vegetable or chicken stock
1 large Maris Piper potato, spiralised
2 tbsp galangal purée (or ginger)
2 tbsp lemongrass, finely chopped
4 kaffir lime leaves
Juice of a lime
2-3 tbsp fish sauce (optional)
2 hot red chillies, sliced
Small bunch coriander
Small bunch basil
Small handful mangetout
6 button mushrooms, sliced
Few slices of ginger

1 Bring the stock to the boil and add all the ingredients except the potatoes, coriander and basil.
2 Simmer for 5 mins then add the potato and cook for 4-5 mins more, until the potato is soft but not falling apart.
3 Serve with the fresh coriander and basil and some extra lime wedges, chilli and fish sauce on the side.
www.lovepotatoes.co.uk

23 SUNDAY

24 MONDAY

25 TUESDAY

26 WEDNESDAY

27 THURSDAY

28 FRIDAY

29 SATURDAY

A magical memory

ONE HUNDRED WOMEN

To mark the centenary of a women's magazine, an exhibition of photos of 100 older women was held in Alexandra Palace. The idea was inspired by the actress Harriet Walter's book in praise of older women. I was one of the 100 women chosen and a photographer came to my house to take my picture, but when I went to see the exhibition I was unable to find it. I was very disappointed and told the editor who phoned the office and found that it had been left behind. She arranged for a minicab to ferry it over and it was hung on the wall.

A few weeks later a tea party was held for the 100 women to meet Harriet Walter and the staff of the magazine who had all baked cakes for the occasion. All of the 100 women had been chosen for their different life experiences so it was very interesting to meet them and talk. A few of them were in their 90s and one was 100 years old. It was a very enjoyable experience which I won't forget.

Colleen Brunton, Enfield

On this week

FEBRUARY 28, 1969: **The British television sitcom On The Buses was broadcast for the first time. Set in a bus depot, how we loved seeing Reg Varney as Stan Butler the bus driver who works the Luxton and District Traction Company along with Jack and Blakey.**

In the garden

Have a slug party!

Why not turn the humdrum into a fun occasion? Pesky slugs are out in full force now - particularly after a wet early spring - so they need showing who's boss. Take your grandchildren out with a bucket and, with guidance, ask them to see how many they can collect in half an hour!

I never knew that!

The internal section of our eardrums are roughly the width of a pencil, yet contain as many as 20,000 hair cells! Hair cells in the cochlea turn sound vibrations into electrical signals, which are sent to the brain to tell us what we are hearing.

Wonderful wildlife on your doorstep!

PIC: ALAMY STOCK PHOTO

NAME: **Fair Isle wren**
HABITAT: **Unique to Fair Isle in Shetland, Scotland.**
DIET: **Insects, worms and berries.**
FAST FACT: **Found only on Fair Isle, in 2017 there were thought to be only about 39 singing males left.**

Recipe of the week

FLUFFY SPELT PANCAKES

SERVES: 8 PREP: 10 MINS COOK: 25 MINS

100g (4oz) spelt flour
2 tsp baking powder
Pinch salt
1 tsp caster sugar
1 egg
150ml (¼ pt) nut milk
A little oil for greasing
Eggs and bacon, to serve

1 Sift the flour into a mixing bowl and mix in the baking powder, salt and sugar.
2 In another bowl, whisk together the egg and milk, then add to the flour and stir until you have a smooth batter. Leave to rest for 15 mins.
3 Heat the griddle pan and lightly brush with oil. Add 4 tbsp of the batter, leaving a space between each, and cook until firm. Turn and cook for 2-3 mins until golden. Repeat with the remaining batter until you have 8 pancakes.
Lakeland

1 SUNDAY

2 MONDAY

3 TUESDAY

4 WEDNESDAY

5 THURSDAY

6 FRIDAY

7 SATURDAY

A magical memory

UPSTAIRS, DOWNSTAIRS

This photo shows my Aunt Nell (fifth from the right) and my Aunt Ada (ninth from the right) who were both in service at the house in the background. My mother, the youngest, followed her sisters into service when she was fourteen as my grandfather didn't want her to work in an office which he considered to be dens of iniquity!

They found work through an agency and sometimes all worked together at the same big house. One of these was Carisbrooke Castle on the Isle of Wight. A few years ago when I visited the Castle I surprised the guide by mentioning an underground passageway that linked the kitchen to the residential rooms. My mother had told us tales of dancing along this passageway, doing the Charleston with the butler!

My sister and I once visited one of my aunts when she was employed at Clarence House, then owned by Lady Patricia Ramsey. We only went to the kitchen, but what I remember most is that the butler brought us a bunch of grapes from the hothouse on a silver salver.

Audrey Warwick, Nottingham

On this week

MARCH 2, 1969: **All eyes were to the sky on this day as Concorde made her maiden flight. The supersonic plane was in the air for just 27 minutes, flying at just 300mph, a fraction of the impressive 1,300mph speeds she would later reach.**

In the garden

Grow your tomatoes with baking soda

If you like to grow tomatoes in your greenhouse, sprinkle a small amount of baking soda onto the soil around where the tomatoes are growing, careful to not get any on the actual fruit. This will lower the acidity of the soil, giving your tomatoes a sweeter taste.

I never knew that!

British novelist Agatha Christie is of course well-known for her best-selling crime novels, but during her writing career she also wrote six other novels under the pseudonym Mary Westmacott. Her daughter Rosalind described the books as bittersweet stories about love.

Wonderful wildlife on your doorstep!

PIC: ALAMY STOCK PHOTO

NAME: **Hare**
HABITAT: **Grassland, farmland and woodland edges throughout the UK.**
DIET: **Grass and other plants, herbs and bark.**
FAST FACT: **Female hares will stand on their hind legs and fight off, or box, unwanted advances from over-enthusiastic males.**

Recipe of the week

RHUBARB, POMEGRANATE AND GINGER SPONGE PUDDING

SERVES: 8 PREP: 20 MINS COOK: 1 HOUR 30 MINS

250g (9oz) rhubarb, sliced
50g (2oz) soft brown muscovado sugar
1 piece stem ginger, finely chopped
50g (2oz) pomegranate seeds
For the sponge:
125g (4½oz) butter
125g (4½oz) caster sugar
2 large eggs, beaten
175g (6oz) self-raising flour
1 tsp baking powder
2 tsp ground ginger
1 tbsp golden syrup
3 tbsp milk
Vanilla custard, to serve

1 Heat the rhubarb with the brown sugar and chopped ginger until tender. Stir in the pomegranate seeds and spoon into the base of a buttered 900ml pudding basin.
2 Cream the butter and caster sugar until pale and fluffy then gradually beat in the eggs.
3 Sift in the flour, baking powder and ground ginger, and fold in with the golden syrup and milk. Pour into the basin and level. Cover with a double layer of baking parchment and foil, with a fold in the middle to allow the pudding to expand.
4 Steam in a large pan for 1½ hours, topping up with water as necessary.
5 Turn out and serve with warmed custard, or cream.
www.waitrose.com/recipes

8 SUNDAY

9 MONDAY

10 TUESDAY

11 WEDNESDAY

12 THURSDAY

13 FRIDAY

14 SATURDAY

A magical memory

THE FIRMEST OF FRIENDS

In this picture my mother, Lily, is on the right in the front row and Vi, the mother of my friend Jill, is on the right of the back row. They became friends when they worked in the same department store and remained friends after both had married and had children. We lived close enough for Jill and me to play together until my parents moved away from Salisbury after the war.

As I was due to take my 11-plus exam it was arranged that I would stay with Jill's parents until the end of the school year. Jill and I had to share a double bed which had a bolster down the middle to avoid any arguments at bedtime! In 1953, when Jill was bedridden with rheumatic fever, I returned to Salisbury to watch the Coronation with her on TV. When I got married three years later, Jill was the only person I wanted as my bridesmaid.

Our mothers remained friends throughout their lives and, now in our eighties, Jill and I still meet regularly and look on each other as surrogate sisters.

Ann Lefley, West Sussex

On this week

MARCH 12, 1969: **She loves you yeah, yeah, yeah! One quarter of the Fab Four, Paul McCartney wed Linda Eastman in London. Dozens of policemen were on hand to fend off teenagers distraught that the last bachelor Beatle was finally tying the knot.**

In the garden

Preserving your daffodils

Whether it's a shop-bought bunch or some you've cut from the garden, preserve those lovely daffodils by mixing 2 tbsp of lemon juice, 1 tbsp of sugar and ½ tsp of bleach into the vase of water to work as plant food so your daffodils will keep shining yellow for as long as possible.

I never knew that!

International Women's Day is celebrated across the globe in different ways. Italians honour the women in their lives by giving them bright yellow Mimosa blossoms, which are a symbol of strength and sensibility. In Berlin it's recognised as a public holiday, while in other countries across the world it's a day to stand up for women's rights.

Wonderful wildlife on your doorstep!

PIC: ALAMY STOCK PHOTO

NAME: **Adder snake**
HABITAT: **Woodland and open countryside.**
DIET: **Small mammals, birds, lizards and frogs.**
FAST FACT. **The adder is the only venomous native snake found in the UK. Thankfully they aren't aggressive and are actually quite shy.**

Recipe of the week

LEMONY CHICKEN, LEEK AND PANCETTA SPAGHETTI CARBONARA

SERVES: 4 PREP: 5 MINS COOK: 10 MINS

2 egg yolks
100ml (4fl oz) single cream
2 unwaxed lemons
60g (2 ½ oz) parmesan, grated
Splash of olive oil, for frying
300g (10 ½ oz) chicken breasts, cut into strips
50g (2oz) smoked pancetta, diced
1 leek, washed and finely sliced, tough outer leaves removed
300g (10 ½ oz) spaghetti
50ml (2fl oz) hot water
Salt and black pepper
1 tbsp lemon thyme, optional

1 For the carbonara sauce, put the egg yolks, cream, the juice of the two lemons and half the Parmesan into a mixing jug and mix together with a fork.
2 Heat a large frying pan, add a splash of olive oil and fry the chicken and pancetta until golden and cooked through. Lower the heat to medium and add the leeks to the pan, and fry until they have softened slightly but are still a vibrant green colour.
3 Cook the spaghetti until it is al dente, drain it. Immediately, toss the pasta in the pan with the leeks, chicken and pancetta, then remove from the heat and add 50ml (2fl oz) of hot water and the carbonara sauce to the pasta and stir together. Season with salt and black pepper.
4 To serve, grate the lemon peel onto the top of the pasta with the rest of the Parmesan and the lemon thyme if using.
www.british-leeks.co.uk

15 SUNDAY

16 MONDAY

17 TUESDAY

18 WEDNESDAY

19 THURSDAY

20 FRIDAY

21 SATURDAY

A magical memory

DEAREST GRANDDAD

My Granddad Newton, pictured here on his 80th birthday with his great-grandchildren, was the best grandfather anyone could wish for. He and Grandma looked after my sister, Janet, and me in the school holidays and every day was an adventure. He had an allotment and we used to help him weigh and bag up the tomatoes to give to the neighbours. I liked his raw rhubarb which probably wasn't very good for my stomach.

It was Granddad who made me my first pair of stilts and a super sledge – I was the envy of all the kids in the street. He taught us to play the piano and my friends were always welcome to join in.

As a special treat we were given a pomegranate with a needle to eat the seeds. Another treat was 'pop' with ice-cream which he frothed up with a whisk to make ice-cream soda. When he visited, he brought us Uncle Joe's mint balls and at Christmas he sneaked us a tiny drop of sherry with the instruction 'not to tell your dad'. I still have such happy memories of him.
Karen Williams, Oldham

On this week

MARCH 15, 1972: **The film The Godfather, starring Marlon Brando and Al Pacino premiered on the big screen in New York. Based on the book by Mario Puzo and directed by Francis Ford Coppola it was an instant smash hit.**

In the garden

Rehoming your pot plants

Before your pot plants start flowering, it's important to move them into a larger pot with fresh compost. You'll be able to tell if the plant needs to move to a bigger home as the roots will most likely be poking out from the base. Moving the plant to a bigger pot will rejuvenate the plant, giving the roots room to grow and spread, leaving the plant to flourish.

I never knew that!

On average, we spend around one third of our lives sleeping and we are the only mammals that put off going to sleep! Cats of course don't have this problem and spend around two thirds of their lifetime in the land of nod!

Wonderful wildlife on your doorstep!

PIC: ALAMY STOCK PHOTO

NAME: **Mute swan**
HABITAT: **Rivers and canals throughout the UK.**
DIET: **Aquatic vegetation, small fish, frogs and worms.**
FAST FACT: **The Queen owns all unmarked mute swans in open water in the UK, but this doesn't apply to Whooper and Bewick's Swans, although they're still protected by law.**

Recipe of the week

ALMOND & CHERRY BAKED OATS

SERVES: 2 PREP: 2 MINS COOK: 20 MINS

80g (3½ oz) porridge oats
2 tbsp ground flaxseed
20g (¾ oz) ground almonds
70g (3oz) Alpro Plain Unsweetened Big Pot
170ml (¼ pt) Alpro Almond Unsweetened drink
½ tsp almond extract (optional)
100g (4oz) frozen pitted cherries (or tinned)
2 tbsp maple syrup, plus extra to serve

1 Preheat the oven to 180°C/350°F/Gas Mark 4.
2 Mix together all the ingredients except the cherries until well combined.
3 Spoon into two small shallow baking dishes.
4 Dot with the cherries pushing them into the oats.
5 Bake in the oven for 20 mins or until set with a lightly coloured crust on top.
6 Drizzle with a little extra maple syrup to serve.
Alpro

22 SUNDAY

23 MONDAY

24 TUESDAY

25 WEDNESDAY

26 THURSDAY

27 FRIDAY

28 SATURDAY

A magical memory

VROOM, VROOM!

People either love or hate motorcycles but my memories of them are all happy ones. When I was a teenager at the end of the war, my boyfriend bought a motorbike with his demob money. With me riding pillion, we were able to visit all the seaside areas that had been off-limits during the war as well as local castles and the Northumbrian countryside. Admittedly, our parents worried about us, but they didn't fuss as long as we dressed warmly and wore goggles. Although they were worn on the race track, crash helmets didn't become compulsory until June 1973.

We soon became avid speedway and road race supporters, following our favourite riders and teams. We arranged our wedding to fit in with the Senior TT races on the Isle of Man. Our hero was Geoff Duke and we were delighted when he won the race in 1952. After the birth of our first baby we added a sidecar to our trusty bike. When our family increased we said a fond farewell to our motorcycling days, but the memories still linger.
Pat Berkshire, Hexham

On this week

MARCH 25, 1950: **Visitors to Hampstead Heath could be forgiven for thinking they'd taken a wrong turn and ended up in Norway as a ski jump, complete with 45 tonnes of snow and 25 skiers was erected by the Central Council of Physical Recreation.**

In the garden

Plant your summer bulbs

With the soil now warming up it's the perfect time to plant your favourite summer bulbs. If your garden is on heavy soil, plant in pots or plant directly in the ground but make sure you label where each bulb has been planted. Plants like lilies and gladioli grow perfectly this season and will look stunning in the summer.

I never knew that!

The shortest airport runway in the world measures just 1,300ft long and can be found on the Caribbean island of Saba. In comparison one of the shortest airport runways in the UK can be found at London City Airport, with a length of 4,948ft. At Scotland's Barra Airport, the beach is the runway and take-off times vary with the tide!

Wonderful wildlife on your doorstep!

PIC: ALAMY STOCK PHOTO

NAME: **Wallaby**
HABITAT: **Woodland and scrubland although they'll feed in open spaces.**
DIET: **Heather, bracken and grasses.**
FAST FACT: **This unexpected UK resident was deliberately introduced into the wild on an island of Loch Lomond, Scotland, but can also be found on the Isle of Man after a pair escaped from a local wildlife park.**

Recipe of the week

LEFTOVER LAMB HOTPOT

SERVES: 4 PREP: 10 MINS COOK: 15 MINS

400g (14oz) baby/salad potatoes (such as Charlotte), each sliced into 3
2 tbsp olive oil
1 onion, roughly chopped
2 carrots, sliced thinly
1 leek, thinly sliced
400g (14oz) leftover roast lamb, cut into chunks
1 tsp plain flour
2 rosemary sprigs
1 tbsp Worcestershire sauce
400ml (14 fl oz) lamb stock

1 Preheat oven to 200°C/400°F/Gas Mark 5.
2 Bring a medium-sized pan of water to the boil, add the sliced potatoes and cook for 5 mins, drain and leave to cool. In a large pan add 1 tbsp of the olive oil and cook the onion, carrot and leek over a medium heat until they start to colour.
3 Add the lamb and continue cooking for a couple more minutes before stirring in the flour. Deglaze with the Worcestershire sauce then pour in the lamb stock and bring to a steady simmer, add the rosemary, leave it ticking away and season to taste.
4 Heat up the last of the olive oil in a large frying pan and cook the sliced blanched potatoes until they start to turn golden.
5 Pour the lamb into a medium-sized oven dish, top with the potatoes, place in the oven and cook for 10-15 mins.
lovepotatoes.co.uk

29 SUNDAY

30 MONDAY

31 TUESDAY

1 WEDNESDAY

2 THURSDAY

3 FRIDAY

4 SATURDAY

A magical memory

MY CONSTANT COMPANION

My cat, Inky, came to live with us after my mother had seen a notice in our local butcher's shop, 'Good homes wanted for four kittens. Free'. Mum said: "I'm sure our Yvonne would love a kitten." With great excitement that evening I opened our front door and the butcher's boy put a little black bundle into my hands.

In the winter Inky loved to sit in a cardboard box on the hearth close to the fire. He used to wait for me on the garden wall when I came home from school at 4.30. Mum said that even after I had started work in London and didn't arrive home until much later, Inky would still jump up on the wall at 4.20 every day.

We once took Inky on a camping holiday to Dymchurch which he thoroughly enjoyed. While we were playing on the sands during the day he slept on my bed. At night he prowled around the campsite and in the morning he would kindly present us with a couple of field mice.

I cried when Inky died just a month before my wedding day. We gave him a simple burial in the garden.   Yvonne Parsons, Exmouth

On this week

APRIL 1, 1957: **Talk about an April Fool's – the BBC had the nation conned with a spoof documentary all about spaghetti crops in Switzerland, presented by Richard Dimbleby. It created mixed reactions from viewers, some of whom enquired where they could purchase a spaghetti bush!**

In the garden

Butterfly magnet

If you're keen to attract plenty of butterflies to your garden over the summer, the best way to draw them in is with buddleia. Make sure you plant your buddleia in direct sunlight and water as you normally would the whole garden and before you know it, they'll be out in full bloom covered with butterflies.

I never knew that!

Because there's no atmosphere in space it's completely silent. The lack of atmosphere also means that there's no wind or rain, so footprints left on the moon by Neil Armstrong and others will remain intact for millions of years to come.

Wonderful wildlife on your doorstep!

PIC: ALAMY STOCK PHOTO

NAME: **Badger**

HABITAT: **Widespread across the UK in woodlands and open fields.**

DIET: **Their staple food is earthworms, but they'll also eat insects, fruit, bulbs and bird eggs.**

FAST FACT: **Badgers are very clean animals and have separate toilet areas within their setts and even spring clean their nests by dragging out old bedding and replacing with new!**

Recipe of the week

BLUEBERRY AND LIME CLAFOUTIS

SERVES: 6 PREP: 10 MIN COOK: 30 MINS

150ml (¼ pt) milk
150ml (¼ pt) single cream
A few drops vanilla essence
4 large eggs
75g (3oz) + 2 tbsp caster sugar
50g (2oz) plain flour
200g (7oz) blueberries
Zest and juice of 1 lime
Icing sugar to dust and a little cream (optional)

1 In a small pan, mix the milk, cream and vanilla and heat until almost boiling.
2 In a large bowl, beat the eggs and sugar until creamy, then add the flour and mix again.
3 Gradually pour the hot milk mixture onto the eggs and beat well. Leave to stand for at least 10 mins or longer if time allows.
4 Preheat the oven to 200°C/400°F/Gas Mark 6. Lightly oil a 23cm (9in) ovenproof dish.
5 Mix the blueberries with 2 tbsp of the caster sugar and the lime zest and juice and scatter over the base of the dish.
6 Pour the batter over the blueberries. Place the dish on a baking sheet and bake for 30 mins until the clafoutis is slightly risen and puffy.
7 Dust with icing sugar and serve warm or cold with cream as desired.
British Lion Eggs

5 SUNDAY

6 MONDAY

7 TUESDAY

8 WEDNESDAY

9 THURSDAY

10 FRIDAY

11 SATURDAY

A magical memory

TRULY BLESSED

As we had tried for twelve years to have a baby, the news of my pregnancy was greeted with great joy by everyone. The sister who was present at the birth told me they liked older mums as they were very stoic and didn't make a fuss. I didn't feel very stoic and when the doctor asked if he could bring a group of students in to watch I replied that I didn't care if the whole hospital came in, I just wanted it to be over!

As Alison was small and a little cold at birth, she was put in an incubator for a few hours. The sister said: "Now I'm going to give you something really nice." Hooray - a cup of tea, I thought, but she went on: "I'm going to give you a lovely wash."

"A cup of tea would be nice, too," I said hopefully and this arrived a few minutes later. The best and most welcome cup of tea I've had in my life.

Four years later, Alison had a brother and I still feel blessed to have two children when some women can't have any.

Wendy Chappell, Havant

On this week

APRIL 5, 1965: **The Academy Awards recognised two icons of the year's films that would go on to become classics as a jubilant Julie Andrews took home Best Actress award for Mary Poppins while Rex Harrison clinched Best Actor for My Fair Lady.**

In the garden

Brighten up your plant pots

Beautifully painted pots can be rather pricey so why not make your plain plant pots bright and bold yourself using acrylic paints? Whether it's a pretty design or creative way of labelling what's inside, you could even rope in the help of your grandchildren if you're taking care of them over the Easter break.

I never knew that!

With one of the oldest transport systems in the world, the London Underground is also one of the largest. There are 270 underground stations and 11 lines that cater for up to five million passenger journeys per day. The whole of London's underground network is around 249 miles long.

Wonderful wildlife on your doorstep!

PIC: ALAMY STOCK PHOTO

NAME: **Muntjac deer**
HABITAT: **Woodland, scrub land and hedgerows.**
DIET: **Shoots, leaves, bramble and raspberry.**
FAST FACT: **Brought from China to Woburn Park, Bedfordshire, in the early 20th Century many were deliberately released across England. Unlike other deer species they breed all year round.**

Recipe of the week

CHICKEN PESTO PASTA

SERVES: 4 PREP: 5 MINS COOK: 35 MINS

6 chicken thigh fillets
250g (9oz) cherry tomatoes
3 tbsp pesto sauce
50g (2oz) toasted pine nuts
300g (10 ½ oz) penne pasta
25g (1oz) pack basil, roughly shredded

1 Heat the oven to 200°C/400°F/Gas Mark 6.
2 Cut each fillet into 4-5 strips and place in a roasting tin with the tomatoes and toss in the pesto sauce. Sprinkle over the pine nuts and bake for 20-25 mins until the chicken is cooked through with no pink meat and the juices run clear.
3 Meanwhile, cook the pasta in boiling water for 10 mins until tender, drain and return to the pan. Add the chicken with all the juices and toss well. Stir in the basil and season to taste.
www.waitrose.com/recipes

12 SUNDAY

13 MONDAY

14 TUESDAY

15 WEDNESDAY

16 THURSDAY

17 FRIDAY

18 SATURDAY

A magical memory

THE WEEKEND STARTED HERE

When I was at school, my weekends began with a sleepover with Nan and Granddad who lived on the Titsey estate in Sussex where Granddad was employed as a carpenter. The bus dropped me close to their cottage and as I closed the gate I could hear Nan singing in the kitchen.

After I had changed out of my uniform, we would give what Nan called 'a quick flick' to the nearby church where my parents had been married and I was christened. While I was busy with my duster, Nan would take the dustpan and brush and sweep all before her. We returned home to find Granddad sitting in his favourite chair watching the popular Western, The Virginian.

After a long day, I would retire to my tiny bedroom to read my library book. As the church clock struck midnight I turned the lights out and the next sound I heard was Nan talking to the man who delivered free milk to everyone who lived on the estate. After breakfast, Nan gave me half of the ten shillings she was paid for cleaning the church before I caught the bus home.

Christine Fyson, Ashford

On this week

APRIL 16, 1953: **Well-wishers waited in the rain to watch the Queen and Duke of Edinburgh launch the new royal yacht Britannia from Clydeside. The yacht went on to become one of the world's most famous ships, serving the Royals for 44 years across 968 official voyages.**

In the garden

EGGcellent eggs

There's no doubt you'll be eating and decorating plenty of eggs this season but don't waste the egg shells. Save them before crushing them up and adding them to soil as natural fertiliser. Sprinkling on egg shells can also deter pests too because of their sharp edges!

I never knew that!

The five Olympic rings represent the five continents of the world. The colours of the rings which are blue, green, yellow, black and red are significant too. At least one of the colours appears on every national flag throughout the world.

Wonderful wildlife on your doorstep!

PIC: ALAMY STOCK PHOTO

NAME: **Beaver**

HABITAT: **Wetlands and rivers, mainly in Scotland.**

DIET: **Shoots, leaves and the stems of waterside vegetation, they'll also fell trees to get to the top foliage.**

FAST FACT: **The largest rodent in Europe, the beaver became extinct during the 16th Century, but since then efforts have been made across the UK to re-introduce them.**

Recipe of the week

HOT CROSS BREAD AND BUTTER PUDDING

SERVES: 6 PREP: 2 MINS COOK: 30-35 MINS

6 hot cross buns
25g (1oz) butter
2 large eggs
250ml (½pt) milk
1 tbsp caster sugar
25g (1oz) flaked almonds

1 Heat the oven to 170°C/ 325°F/ Gas Mark 3.
2 Cut the hot cross buns in half and butter the cut sides, sandwich together again and place in a baking dish.
3 Beat the eggs, milk and sugar together and pour over the hot cross buns.
4 Scatter the flaked almonds over the dish and bake for 30-35 minutes until just set.
Aldi

19 SUNDAY

20 MONDAY

21 TUESDAY

22 WEDNESDAY

23 THURSDAY

24 FRIDAY

25 SATURDAY

A magical memory

A LIVERPOOL FAN

I am on the left of this picture taken outside Saint Katharine's teacher training college in Liverpool when my friends and I were invited back for a reunion. I attended the college from 1974 to 1977 and moved back to the Midlands when I acquired my first teaching post in a primary school.

I have many fond memories of the three years I spent in the vibrant city of Liverpool which has more museums, art galleries and listed buildings than anywhere else outside London. During my time there I visited many of its clubs and music venues including The Cavern, birthplace of The Beatles. I also went to some of the places such as Penny Lane and Strawberry Field that inspired some of their most memorable songs.

One of my greatest passions is football and, as an avid Liverpool supporter, I spent many enjoyable hours watching my team at Anfield stadium.

After leaving St Katharine's I worked full-time for twelve years before leaving to bring up my daughter, Heather, and my son, Greg.
Chris Wileman, Walsall

On this week

APRIL 19, 1956: **Grace Kelly looked resplendent and just a touch nervous in her ivory gown of silk taffeta and lace as she wed Prince Rainier III of Monaco before driving through the streets of Monte Carlo in an open-top car waving to fans.**

In the garden

Butterfly house

With the number of British butterflies in decline, it's important we make a special space for these beautiful creatures in our garden ahead of summer. Build or buy your own butterfly house and place in a sunny but sheltered spot away from the wind about six ft up from the ground. Ensure it's close to nectar rich flowers so they've got plenty to feed on.

I never knew that!

Whatever your brew of choice, whether it's black, green or white, all tea comes from the same species of plant, called Camellia Sinensis. Of course, us Brits love a nice cuppa and between us we drink a staggering 165 million cups a day - that's 60.2 billion a year!

Wonderful wildlife on your doorstep!

PIC: ALAMY STOCK PHOTO

NAME: **Sand lizard**
HABITAT: **Sandy areas including heathland and dunes.**
DIET: **Slugs, spiders and insects plus fruit and flower heads.**
FAST FACT: **One of the UK's rarest lizards, in spring the males emerge from hibernation and change colour from brown to bright green ready for breeding season.**

Recipe of the week

BERRILICIOUS OAT PANCAKES

SERVES: 2 PREP: 15 MINS (PLUS 30 MINUTES RESTING THE BATTER) COOK: 5 MINS

1 tbsp ground flaxseed
140g (5oz) plain flour
½ tsp salt
270ml (½ pt) Alpro Oat Unsweetened drink
250g (9oz) mixed frozen berries
1 tbsp maple syrup
1 tbsp vegan butter
Alpro Plain Unsweetened Big Pot to serve

1 Place the flaxseed in a small bowl with 3 tbsp hot water and whisk together. Put to one side for 5 mins to gel together.
2 Whisk together the flour, salt, ground flaxseed and Alpro Oat Unsweetened until perfectly smooth.
3 Rest the batter for 30 mins. When you come to use the batter you may need to add a splash more Alpro Oat Unsweetened to loosen a little until you have a good consistency.
4 Add the frozen berries to a medium-sized saucepan and heat through until hot and thawed. Add in the maple syrup and blitz with a stick blender until smooth.
5 Heat a little of the vegan butter in a non-stick pancake pan over a medium heat. When the pan is hot add in a ladleful of the batter, swirling to coat the pan and cook for 2 mins or until the pancake can be loosened and flipped to cook the other side for 30 secs. Continue with the remaining batter.
6 Serve the pancakes with a drizzle of the warmed berry sauce and a dollop of Alpro Plain Unsweetened Big Pot.
Alpro

26 SUNDAY

27 MONDAY

28 TUESDAY

29 WEDNESDAY

30 THURSDAY

1 FRIDAY

2 SATURDAY

A magical memory

FOREVER FRIENDS

Shirley and I have seen one another through births, deaths, marriages, divorce, good and bad times. We met as children in Dagenham and her first words to me were: "Can I have a push of your doll's pram?"

When war broke out we were both evacuated, but were soon back home again. Together we witnessed the London Blitz, collected shrapnel and dressed up in old lace curtains. We argued frequently, most days ending with: "I'm never going to speak to you again!"

We had a lot of freedom to wander around. On Sundays we went to any place of worship that took our fancy. The parish church was a favourite and after the service we toured the graveyard redistributing the flowers on the graves more equally 'to make it fair'.

When we were older, we both worked as receptionists at the local photographer's shop. We learned to drive which was a novelty at the time and had some interesting excursions in Shirley's little blue mini. Now that she lives in Hampshire and I'm still in Essex we keep in touch by phone, email and text.

Gwyneth M Lowe, Brentwood

On this week

APRIL 26, 1962: **The first US rocket landed on the far side of the moon, with the intention of capturing the first ever pictures of the lunar surface but a technical fault meant that disappointingly no pictures and just a patchy radio signal came back.**

In the garden

Sowing and growing sweet peas

Start by sowing your sweet pea seeds indoors in old cardboard toilet roll holders. Keep them well watered before moving them into the garden in nutrient-rich soil next to something they can climb up such as a cane or old ladder. Cuttings of your sweet peas will smell beautiful in dainty vases around the house.

I never knew that!

George Lazenby was the youngest actor to play James Bond at the age of 30 in On Her Majesty's Secret Service (1969). Roger Moore was the oldest, in A View to Kill aged 57. Italian actress Monica Bellucci became one of the oldest Bond Girls, or Bond Women, when at 51 she was cast in Spectre (2015).

Wonderful wildlife on your doorstep!

PIC: ALAMY STOCK PHOTO

NAME: **Grey squirrel**
HABITAT: **Parks, woodlands and gardens across the UK.**
DIET: **Acorns, bulbs, nuts, tree shoots and fungi.**
FAST FACT: **The grey squirrel doesn't harm the red squirrel, but they're better at food gathering and can carry a disease that red squirrels can't recover from.**

Recipe of the week

RADISH AND CELERY BAGEL

SERVES: 2 PREP: 5 MINS COOK: 2-5 MINS

2 seeded bagels
120g (4½ oz) hummus
1 stick of celery, sliced
4-6 radishes, sliced
½ avocado, de-stoned, peeled and sliced
½ pack salad cress

1 Toast the bagels. Spread one side of each bagel thickly with hummus.
2 Top with layers of sliced celery, radish, avocado, then finish with some salad cress.
www.lovecelery.co.uk

3 SUNDAY

4 MONDAY

5 TUESDAY

6 WEDNESDAY

7 THURSDAY

8 FRIDAY

9 SATURDAY

A magical memory

WE WERE EASTENDERS

Leatherdale Street in Stepney where I grew up is no longer on the map as it was part of the post-war clearance of the East End. Our house, number 23, was shared by three families. My mum, dad and me had the ground floor - three rooms with a yard at the back, a shed and an outside loo.

One room was our kitchen, bathroom and living room. This was where Mum cooked and did the laundry, Dad smoked and read the newspaper, and we all listened to the radio. It was also where we took turns to have a strip wash at the sink every morning. Room number two was our shared bedroom with a single and a double bed. In the winter, the blankets were boosted with outdoor coats and newspapers.

Room number three was the most interesting. It was the front room and had an ancient three-piece suite, a dining table and tiled fireplace, but it was hardly ever used. The fire was only lit on special occasions and I remember very few of them. At Christmas we went to my aunt's house because it was bigger and had a piano.
Dee Gordon, Southend

On this week

MAY 3, 1951: **King George opened the iconic 1951 Festival of Britain and the Royal Festival Hall at London's Southbank. It celebrated Britain's contribution to the arts, science, industry and technology and helped whip up the spirits of a war-weary nation.**

In the garden

Herb garden

From basil to rosemary, mint and sage, season your food with tasty fresh herbs grown in the garden. Place your herb garden in a spot where they'll get plenty of sunlight in close proximity to your kitchen so you can pop out to cut some herbs while you cook. At the end of the season, you can freeze them to enjoy in the winter months.

I never knew that!

Olivia Newton-John and Michelle Pfeiffer were also considered for the role of Donna in the smash hit Mamma Mia films. Thankfully it was Meryl Streep who sang her way into our hearts, as did Cher who plays Donna's mum Ruby. In real-life though Cher is actually only three years older than her on-screen daughter Donna!

Wonderful wildlife on your doorstep!

PIC: ALAMY STOCK PHOTO

NAME: **Basking shark**

HABITAT: **Coastal waters off the coast of Cornwall, Dorset, the Isle of Man and the Scottish Hebrides from May to October.**

DIET: **Zooplankton, small fish and invertebrates.**

FAST FACT: **Unlike other sharks, these gentle giants feed using a ram filter feeding method, where they swim with their mouths wide open, taking in food and filtering out water through their gills.**

Recipe of the week

WENSLEYDALE & CRANBERRY CHEESE PARCELS

SERVES: 4 PREP: 5 MINS COOK: 20 MINS

150g (5oz) Wensleydale & cranberry cheese
1 packet of ready-made puff or filo pastry
1 tbsp melted butter to glaze

1 Place small wedges of the Wensleydale and cranberry cheese in squares of pastry and fold in the corners to make little bundles. Cover with melted butter to glaze.
2 Bake in a hot oven for 20 mins until golden brown.
3 Serve with a rocket salad dressed with your favourite chutney.
www.wensleydale.co.uk

10 SUNDAY

11 MONDAY

12 TUESDAY

13 WEDNESDAY

14 THURSDAY

15 FRIDAY

16 SATURDAY

A magical memory

MY BABY DOLL

The only doll I ever possessed is now seventy years old. Santa brought her to me in 1948 when I was aged three. It's possible she might be even older if she was bought secondhand as my parents, like many others, were still suffering some hardships after the war.

She is made of china and was dressed in a pale blue jacket lined in pink with a matching bonnet. When I was five I was given a hand-me-down pram and loved to push my doll around our huge garden. In the summer I would sit her under the apple tree and watch the butterflies and bees.

Over the years, she has survived seven house moves and has lost her long eyelashes and the ability to say 'Mama' as well as suffering a tiny chip on her big toe. But I have updated her attire and she looks lovely.

These days she is kept safely wrapped in a secure container under my bed. I never had a daughter but I am hoping that one day my two grandsons will have daughters who will enjoy my doll as much as I did.

Sylvie Washington, Burnham on Sea

On this week

MAY 16, 1955: **Olga Korbut, the waif-like USSR gymnast who was nicknamed the 'sparrow from Minsk' and won huge popularity along with three gold medals at the 1972 Munich Olympics, was born in Belarus. She's often credited with changing the face of gymnastics for good.**

In the garden

Maintaining hanging baskets

Keep your hanging basket moist by soaking a nappy in water and placing it in the base of the hanging basket before planting your flowers in the compost. This will help retain plenty of moisture when the weather gets dry and will continue to soak up water every time it's watered.

I never knew that!

The shortest distance across the Dover strait between England and France is only 20.7 miles, from northeast Dover to Cap Gris Nez. The Channel Tunnel itself is 31.4 miles long, with the longest undersea section of any tunnel in the world. It took six years and cost £4.65 billion to construct and there are actually three tunnels – two for trains and a service tunnel for emergencies.

Wonderful wildlife on your doorstep!

PIC: ALAMY STOCK PHOTO

NAME: **Blue tit**
HABITAT: **Common throughout the UK in woodland, parks and gardens.**
DIET: **Insects, especially caterpillars, nuts and seeds.**
FAST FACT: **Blue tits stay here in the UK all year round and don't tend to stray far from where they were hatched.**

Recipe of the week

PEA, MINT AND FETA FRITTATA

SERVES: 4 PREP: 5 MINS COOK: 15 MINS

150g (5oz) frozen peas
8 eggs
80ml (3fl oz) milk
Handful of fresh mint leaves
Salt and pepper
1 tbsp olive oil
100g (4oz) feta cheese

1 Preheat the oven to 200°C/400°F/Gas Mark 6.
2 Boil the peas for five mins in a saucepan of water. Drain and set aside.
3 Whisk the eggs and milk together in a large bowl. Stir in the peas and mint. Season with a pinch of salt and pepper.
4 Heat the olive oil over a medium heat in a large, ovenproof frying pan. Pour in the egg mixture and cook for 4-5 mins to cook the base and the sides.
5 Crumble the feta on top and place in the oven for 10-15 mins until the top is golden and cheese is bubbling.
www.eggrecipes.co.uk

17 SUNDAY

18 MONDAY

19 TUESDAY

20 WEDNESDAY

21 THURSDAY

22 FRIDAY

23 SATURDAY

A magical memory

OUR MAY DAY PARADE

My treasured childhood memory is of the 1954 May Day celebrations in my home town of Rhyl. I was aged nine and proud to be chosen as crown bearer to the May Queen Elect, Gwyneth.

I was following in a long-held family tradition of being involved in the festivities as I had been preceded by my grandfather, my sister June and my brothers Alfred and Billy.

The celebrations involved sixty-six local children appearing in two shows (one in the afternoon and one in the early evening) at the famous Rhyl Pavilion. I appeared in both shows, singing, tap dancing and doing comedy sketches.

The highlight of the day for us children was the parade along the promenade with twenty-two floats led by mounted marshals, the local fire brigade and the Rhyl Silver Prize Band. Each float bore a visiting Carnival Queen surrounded by her court. We were so excited by the huge crowd - it seemed that the whole town had turned out to cheer us on that happy, sunny day.

John Nicholls, Sedgefield

On this week

MAY 20, 1932: **Amelia Earhart became the first woman to fly solo across the Atlantic. Flying from Newfoundland to Londonderry she travelled 2,026 miles in 13 hours. Five years later she would go missing trying to fly her twin-engine plane around the equator.**

In the garden

Make a bug hotel

Building a home for bugs is a great way of creating a safe hideaway for our creepy crawly friends. Pile up different old bricks, planks of wood or pallets no more than a metre off the ground. You'll then need to fill in the gaps with bark chippings and dry leaves to make it a great resting place for all bugs, from centipedes to ladybirds.

I never knew that!

Dentures made from animal teeth and bone date as far back as 2500BC but some of the earliest dentures created in Japan in the early 16th Century were carved entirely from wood! After experimentation with ivory, animal horn and teeth, the first porcelain dentures didn't appear until the 18th Century, when thankfully dentures began to resemble real teeth.

Wonderful wildlife on your doorstep!

PIC: ALAMY STOCK PHOTO

NAME: **Rabbit**

HABITAT: **Widespread across grassland, farmland and woodland.**

DIET: **Grass, leafy weeds, crops and even tree bark.**

FAST FACT: **Rabbits are not actually native to Britain, but are thought to have been introduced in the 12th Century by the Normans.**

Recipe of the week

FETA AND GRILLED PEACH SALAD WITH TOASTED SEEDS

SERVES: 2 PREP: 15 MINS COOK: 4 MINS

1 peach or nectarine, stoned, thickly sliced
1 pack mixed salad leaves
1 little gem lettuce, leaves torn
1 tbsp extra-virgin olive oil
Juice half a lemon
120g (4½oz) feta cheese
1x 25g (1oz) pack of Munchy Seeds Omega Sprinkles

1 First grill the peach. Heat a griddle pan on a high heat and grill for 2 mins on each side then set aside to cool.
2 Put the salad leaves and little gem lettuce in a large bowl. Drizzle over the extra-virgin olive oil and squeeze over the lemon juice. Stir well to combine.
3 To assemble, divide the salad between two plates, scatter over the grilled peach, crumble over the feta and top with Omega Sprinkles.
Munchy Seeds

24 SUNDAY

25 MONDAY

26 TUESDAY

27 WEDNESDAY

28 THURSDAY

29 FRIDAY

30 SATURDAY

A magical memory

NICE WORK!

This photo of me (on the left) with my friend Irene holds happy memories, taking me back to the summer of 1969 when I went with a friend to work as a waitress at a family-run hotel in Great Yarmouth.

There were nine of us girls, hailing from as far away as Yorkshire, Lancashire and Leicestershire and we jogged along together very happily. We served all the meals as well as being on a rota for morning coffee and nightcaps such as Horlicks, served in the lounge. Once our tables were set ready for the next meal we could do our own thing. Often we headed to the beach to relax in the sun or swim in the sea. I took driving lessons in my spare time.

Our food and accommodation were provided so we always had money to spend. Our living area was basic, but comfortable. We shared a room for two with bunk beds. The job was from April to October with older guests coming at the beginning and end of the season and we met some lovely people. It was a truly fulfilling experience.
Heather McEwen, Norwich

On this week

MAY 26, 1980: **Who shot JR? That was the question on everyone's lips when the last episode of season 3 of Dallas aired in the UK showing the murder of JR. We'd have to wait months to find out his ex-lover Kristin was the culprit.**

In the garden

Lovely lavender

It not only makes for a welcoming aroma when people enter your home but lavender has so many amazing uses – it's definitely worth having some in your garden around the front door. You can use indoors, from leaving small bunches around the home to spread the scent, to crushing some lavender up in a small bag to pop under your pillow at night to help you drift off.

I never knew that!

The fastest speed recorded by a race horse was clocked at 43.97 mph over two furlongs. The American thoroughbred called Winning Brew was awarded the Guinness World record for the highest speed ever on a racecourse in 2008.

Wonderful wildlife on your doorstep!

PIC: ALAMY STOCK PHOTO

NAME: **Nightingale**
HABITAT: **Varied habitats, they arrive in the UK in April and stay for the summer.**
DIET: **Fruit, seeds and insects.**
FAST FACT: **Male nightingale birds sing to attract females, but to keep their nests safe you won't hear them sing during nesting season.**

Recipe of the week

MIXED BERRY AND SUPER SEED SMOOTHIE

SERVES: 1 PREP: 5 MINS COOK: NONE

1 frozen banana
200ml (7fl oz) almond milk
60g (2½ oz) strawberries
60g (2½ oz) blueberries
40g (1½ oz) blackberries
1 tbsp Linwoods flaxseed, sunflower, pumpkin, sesame seeds and goji berries mix
1 tbsp Linwoods hemp seeds (optional)

1 Place all the ingredients into a blender, adding the almond milk first to make blending easier.
2 Blend well until completely smooth.
3 Pour into a glass and enjoy.
Linwoods Health foods

31 SUNDAY

1 MONDAY

2 TUESDAY

3 WEDNESDAY

4 THURSDAY

5 FRIDAY

6 SATURDAY

A magical memory

MY UNUSUAL BIRTHDAY

Most children dream of birthday parties with gifts and cakes with candles but I spent my fifth birthday among the dreaming spires of Oxford. I was a Forces' child and as we had recently moved I didn't know enough people to invite to a party so my mother found a different way of celebrating.

We went with a friend to visit her brother who was studying at the university and our red outfits really stood out among the undergraduates' dark gowns. This picture was taken in the deer park at Magdalen College where I couldn't take my eyes off the white hart in the enclosure behind us. We also visited the college's chapel with its stunning stained glass windows and Gothic architecture.

Later we went to the Junior Common Room bar for snacks where a bemused student asked me what I was reading (studying). I immediately replied: "Noddy!" which everyone found hilarious.

We ended my unusual birthday with a magical stroll along the riverbank as the sun bathed the dreaming spires in a golden light.
Charmaine Fletcher via email

On this week

JUNE 2, 1953: **Queen Elizabeth II is crowned in a spectacular ceremony in Westminster Abbey in front of more than 8,000 guests. Meanwhile three million people lined the streets to catch a glimpse of the new monarch as she made her way to Buckingham Palace.**

In the garden

Natural ways to deter pests

Toxic pellets and sprays might be good at getting rid of unwanted garden visitors but they are also poisonous to other animals such as cats, dogs and hedgehogs. Create a natural remedy using a range of homemade concoctions such as salt-water spray or eucalyptus oil and also neem oil mixed with soap and warm water in a spray bottle.

I never knew that!

Stonehenge is older than the Egyptian pyramids, but only in parts. History tells us that the pyramids were built over a span of 85 years from around 2560BC. The bank and ditch surrounding Stonehenge were constructed around 3100BC, but the first stones were erected later somewhere between 2400 and 2200 BC. The Stonehenge we recognise today was created between 1930BC and 1600BC.

Wonderful wildlife on your doorstep!

PIC: ALAMY STOCK PHOTO

NAME: **Small White Butterfly**
HABITAT: **Widespread across the UK in gardens and allotments.**
DIET: **Cabbages as caterpillars and flower nectar as adults.**
FAST FACT: **Often called the cabbage white butterfly due to its love of cabbages, the small white is often confused with the large white butterfly. Small whites are smaller and don't have black wing tips.**

Recipe of the week

PAN-FRIED SALMON WITH RADISH AND AVOCADO SALAD

SERVES: 1 PREP: 10 MINS COOK: 15 MINS

For the dressing:
1 tbsp extra-virgin olive oil
½ tsp Dijon mustard
2 tsp lemon juice
Salt and pepper
For the salad:
1 x 100g (4oz) salmon fillet
8 mixed radishes, cut into quarters
1 little gem lettuce, broken into leaves
1 tbsp frozen peas, defrosted
½ avocado, peeled and sliced
Squeeze of lemon juice
1 tbsp pumpkin seeds, toasted in a dry frying pan
Salt and pepper
Olive oil cooking spray

1 Mix together the dressing ingredients in a screw-top jar. Shake until combined and set aside.
2 Assemble the salad onto a plate. Squeeze the lemon juice over the avocado to prevent it browning and set it aside.
3 Season the salmon. Spritz a non-stick frying pan with cooking spray. When it's smoking, add the salmon, skin side down and cook for 3-5 mins, until the skin is brown. Flip over and continue cooking from 2-4 mins until the flesh has turned a paler pink.
4 Place the salmon on top of the salad. Sprinkle with a few more pumpkin seeds, drizzle over the dressing and serve.
www.lovethecrunch.com

7 SUNDAY

8 MONDAY

9 TUESDAY

10 WEDNESDAY

11 THURSDAY

12 FRIDAY

13 SATURDAY

A magical memory

SUNDAY SCHOOL OUTING

Here I am with my mum when I was eight years old in 1949. The photo was taken on our annual seaside treat – a Sunday School outing to Clacton-on-Sea. It was always a memorable day. I was so excited that I wore my woollen swimsuit to bed the night before!

The street photographers were always there, waiting to take pictures of the holidaymakers and daytrippers like ourselves. We were able to collect the photos later in the afternoon after they had been developed. Not like today's instant photos and selfies taken on mobile phones, but it gave us something to look forward to.

We always seemed to be lucky enough to have a hot, sunny day, perfect for bathing in the sea and building sandcastles. On one of these outings, my cousins dug a big hole and I put my legs in then wasn't able to get them out again! These are lovely, lasting memories to be sure.

Hazel Moysey, Kingston-upon-Thames

On this week

JUNE 10, 1922: **Judy Garland was born in Grand Rapids, Minnesota. Originally named Frances Ethel Gumm she followed her vaudevillian parents into the world of song and dance to become one of the most iconic – if tragic – performers of all time.**

In the garden

Growing veggies

It's not only healthier and cheaper to grow your own veg rather than buy it, but homegrown vegetables also taste far better. Grow yours in raised plant beds in rich soil, aiming to arrange your plants in triangles rather than squares to utilise the whole space, fitting more plants in each bed.

I never knew that!

The Queen doesn't hold a passport, even though she's travelled all over the world! She doesn't hold a driving licence either and is the only person who's allowed to drive without one. She continues to drive on her estates, although royal protocol insists that she's chauffeured to royal engagements. All other members of the Royal Family do require passports, however.

Wonderful wildlife on your doorstep!

PIC: ALAMY STOCK PHOTO

NAME: **Puffin**

HABITAT: **Grassy cliffs from March to August in selected spots across the UK.**

DIET: **Fish including herring, white hake and sand eels.**

FAST FACT: **Puffins are excellent swimmers and can dive down to a depth of 60 metres, using both their wings and webbed feet to help them swim.**

Recipe of the week

SUPERBERRIES PARFAIT

SERVES: 10 PREP: 15 MINS FREEZE: 6 HOURS

2 bananas, peeled
1.5kg (3lbs) Greek yogurt
4 tbsp maple syrup
330g (12oz) frozen mixed berries
300g (10½ oz) strawberries, sliced
1 tsp Bioglan Superfoods Superberries powder

1 Line a loaf tin with cling film. Mash the bananas until smooth and then stir into the yogurt along with the maple syrup.
2 Fold two-thirds of the frozen berries, strawberries and the Superberries powder through the yogurt to give a ripple effect.
3 Pour into the loaf tin, cover with cling film and freeze for at least 6 hours until set.
4 Before serving, leave to stand for 15-20 mins, remove from the tin and peel off the clingfilm.
5 Top with the remaining berries, slice and serve.
bioglan.co.uk

14 SUNDAY

15 MONDAY

16 TUESDAY

17 WEDNESDAY

18 THURSDAY

19 FRIDAY

20 SATURDAY

A magical memory

FIRST TIME FLYING

This is me, aged seven, coming off the plane on the Isle of Man in 1973. Behind me are my mum and my dad carrying my little brother, Alan. Our previous holidays had been to Blackpool, travelling there by car. As it was our first time flying, we felt extremely glamorous and had got dressed up for the journey. I am wearing my new Clark's sandals with my favourite navy dress and carrying my bucket and spade, keen to go to the beach straightaway. I can't imagine any airline allowing a child to take a bucket and spade on board today.

Mum had told me that our destination had a big beach and I'd be able to build sandcastles. I loved building ones with lots of turrets, decorated with as many different types of shells as I could find. My memories of that holiday are of endless sunny days, the big red water wheel, a trip on a steam train and a fabulous park with swings. Someday, I intend to return to the Isle of Man and when I do I will build a sandcastle in memory of our family holiday there.

Sharon Haston, Falkirk

On this week

JUNE 14, 1961: **The Ministry of Transport announced today the introduction of new push-button controlled 'panda' crossings on roads to reduce pedestrian accidents. These crossings were installed in 1962 but the idea was abandoned the following year as they caused confusion.**

In the garden

Feeding the grass

Believe it or not, one of the best ways to protect grass from infections is to use pennies. Copper is an effective fungicide which can protect grass from infections. By burying a few copper coins just under the surface your lawn, the metal will eventually destroy fungal spores in the soil, benefitting your garden for years to come.

I never knew that!

Sindy, the doll from British company Pedigree Toys was created in 1963 as a more wholesome rival to Barbie. Her girl next door good looks and fashionable clothes were a hit with young girls during the Sixties and just like her slogan, she really did become the girl we liked to dress.

Wonderful wildlife on your doorstep!

PIC: ALAMY STOCK PHOTO

NAME: **Peacock butterfly**
HABITAT: **Gardens and countryside, particularly nettles and the Buddleia plant.**
DIET: **The caterpillars eat nettles, while butterflies eat flower nectar.**
FAST FACT: **As well as flashing their eye-like markings to scare off predators, peacock butterflies also make a hissing sound as a deterrent.**

Recipe of the week

KALE, GOAT'S CHEESE AND NEW POTATO SALAD

SERVES: 4 PREP: 5 MINS COOK: 45 MINS

10ml extra-virgin olive oil
200g (7oz) Cornish (or other) new potatoes
150g (5oz) raw beetroot, peeled and quartered
200g (7oz) kale
80g (3oz) peas
120g (4½oz) asparagus
Goat's cheese cut into 4 round slices
Balsamic glaze (to serve)

1 Preheat the oven to 200°C/400°F/Gas Mark 6.
2 Drizzle a little oil into the roasting tin and put in the oven for a couple of mins to get hot. Meanwhile, place the potatoes in the pre-heated roasting tin with the beetroot and return to the oven for 40-45 mins.
3 Heat a little oil in a heavy-based frying pan. Stir fry the kale for 4 mins and then add the peas and asparagus for a further 3-4 mins. Grill the goat's cheese for 2-3 mins on each side or until lightly browned.
4 Combine all the ingredients together, season with sea salt and black pepper and serve onto each plate. Place the grilled goat's cheese on top. Drizzle with balsamic glaze to serve.

Cornish Potatoes

21 SUNDAY

22 MONDAY

23 TUESDAY

24 WEDNESDAY

25 THURSDAY

26 FRIDAY

27 SATURDAY

A magical memory

CORNISH HISTORY

To celebrate my birthday, my Cornish husband, John, and I visited Geevor Mine which is one of the largest preserved mines in the country and a world heritage site.

I was thrilled as we approached and I saw the skeletal ironwork stark against the skyline. The two-acre site has a number of listed buildings as well as a rock museum. We went on an underground tour, dressed in blue overalls and brightly coloured helmets to protect us from falling debris and dust. A guide with a lamp attached to his helmet led us down the steps through the old mine workings into a long, narrow tunnel. It was cold and damp and I was almost bent double as we went deeper. I imagined the ghosts of past miners hard at work, shovelling, sweating, setting dynamite and eating their 'croust' (Cornish pasties) when they had a break.

It seemed an eternity before we eventually emerged into brilliant sunlight, fresh air and the blue ocean sparkling below. It had been an exciting journey into Cornwall's industrial past.
Diana Manning, Campbeltown

On this week

JUNE 21, 1982: **Prince William Arthur Philip Louis was born at St Mary's Hospital London where his own children would later come into the world. Crowds cheered as Prince Charles and Princess Diana proudly showed off their first son on the hospital steps.**

In the garden
Plant survival tip

Keeping potted plants moist throughout the dry months can be hard, especially if you're keen to reduce the amount of water you're using. You'll need another nappy for this clever tip. Cut away the outside of the nappy and rub the cotton fibres between your hands to release the absorbing granules. Mix them with water before adding to your compost.

I never knew that!

Nail polish was used in China as far back as 3000 BC. Formulas then were made up of ingredients such as beeswax, egg whites and vegetable dyes – making them not quite as long-lasting as what we've become accustomed to! Colour choice was important and in ancient Egypt red nails signified a higher class.

Wonderful wildlife on your doorstep!

PIC: SHUTTERSTOCK

NAME: **Norfolk hawker dragonfly**
HABITAT: **Mainly found in undisturbed wetland areas of the Norfolk Broads as females favour the Water-soldier plant to lay their eggs.**
DIET: **Flying insects.**
FAST FACT: **This rare dragonfly spends up to two years as dragonfly larvae in water, before moulting into an adult.**

Recipe of the week

RASPBERRY FRO-YO

SERVES: 6 PREP: 10 MINS FREEZE: 1 HOUR

350g (12oz) raspberries, washed and dried
500g (1lb 2oz) Greek yogurt
200g (7oz) condensed milk

1 Put the raspberries in a lidded container and freeze until solid.
2 Once solid put them in a food processor and blitz until finely chopped. Take out 3-4 tbsp and keep in the freezer until ready to serve.
3 Add the Greek yogurt and condensed milk to the processor and whizz until everything is combined. The raspberries will have frozen the other ingredients so serve 'soft scoop' straight away or tip into a freezer container to firm up.
4 Serve scoops of the frozen mixture with the reserved raspberry bits sprinkled over the top.
Berryworld

28 SUNDAY

29 MONDAY

30 TUESDAY

1 WEDNESDAY

2 THURSDAY

3 FRIDAY

4 SATURDAY

A magical memory

THAT LONG HOT SUMMER

My brother, who had a new camera, took this photo of our mother in the searing summer heat of 1966. Feeling hot and bothered, she was very reluctant to pose by the door to our conservatory, but I'm so glad she did.

I was eight years old at the time and loved the false hair piece she is wearing. The colour was called 'fox' and it had a silver gloss that made it look very glamorous. Hairpieces were commonplace at the time, but my mum was the first person in our road to have one. I would sit and watch in awe as the hairdresser reattached it every week. Oblivious to all the laborious hours it took to fix it, I dreamed of having a hairdo like that when I was grown up. (I never did - what with the advent of feather cuts and pageboy styles.)

Mum was wearing her hairpiece when we watched England winning the football World Cup on TV. Despite jumping up and down in elation, her hairpiece stayed immaculately in place!
Heather Moulson, Twickenham

On this week

JULY 3, 1969: **Lulu the strong-willed elephant made one of the most iconic moments of children's television on tonight's episode of Blue Peter as she ran rings around the presenters before spending a penny on the floor and pulling down her handler.**

In the garden

Making a water butt

Make your own miniature water butt using an old six-pint milk carton. Cut the very bottom off the carton ensuring it's clean with the lid still on. Use cable ties or twine to tie the carton to a post or fence panel with the lid pointing down. When it rains, your homemade water butt will collect any rain water ready for the next time you water the garden.

I never knew that!

The title of 'tallest building in the world' is currently held by Dubai's Burj Khalifa, which is a staggering 828m (2,716ft 6 in) tall. It takes a team of 36 window cleaners three months to get every window sparkling! This record is set to be broken this year though by Saudi Arabia's Jeddah Tower, which will scale a jaw-dropping 1000m (3,280ft).

Wonderful wildlife on your doorstep!

PIC: ALAMY STOCK PHOTO

NAME: **Curlew**
HABITAT: **Widespread along the UK coastline.**
DIET: **Worms, shrimps and shellfish.**
FAST FACT: **The largest wading bird in Europe, the tip of the curlew's beak acts independently and is used to feel around in mud for food.**

Recipe of the week

VEGAN PLATTER

SERVES: 4 PREP: 10 MINS COOK: 20 MINS

1 packet of pressed or extra-firm tofu, sliced into 4 pieces and dried thoroughly
4 corn on the cobs
2 slightly under-ripe avocados, cut in half and pitted
6-8 stone fruits eg plums and peaches
Oil with a higher smoke point eg sunflower or rapeseed
2 tbsp barbecue sauce

1 Pre-heat your barbecue or grill.
2 Drizzle the tofu, corn, avocados and fruit with a little oil.
3 Add the tofu to the barbecue. Flip every 5 mins for a total cooking time of 20 mins. Drizzle with barbecue sauce for the last 10 mins.
4 After the first tofu flip, add the corn, turning as the kernels start to brown. They will take about 10-12 mins.
5 During the last 5 mins of the tofu cooking, add the avocado and fruit cut side down for 3-4 mins.
6 Serve seasoned with a little salt and pepper.
Myvega.co.uk

5 SUNDAY

6 MONDAY

7 TUESDAY

8 WEDNESDAY

9 THURSDAY

10 FRIDAY

11 SATURDAY

A magical memory

TAWNY OWL AND SNOWY OWL

I joined the Brownies when I was seven, but it was not long before the war started and I was evacuated. That was the end of the Brownies for me until my daughter joined and I was roped in as a helper. I was asked to do my Brownie Leader training and took over the 223rd Birmingham Pack as Brown Owl.

I enjoyed running the Pack, but hadn't realised how much time and effort it took. The meetings only lasted an hour, but the preparation could take much longer, especially if we were making Mother's Day gifts or greetings cards for Christmas or Easter. My husband and teenage son were soon co-opted to test badges such as swimming or safety in the home. When she was old enough, my daughter did her training and joined me, being called Snowy Owl by the Brownies.

I ran the Pack for seventeen years and although it was sometimes hard work it gave me a lot of pleasure. I would recommend it to anyone who can spare the time as it is very rewarding.
Eileen Gibbins, Kidderminster

On this week

JULY 9, 1984: **The historic York Minster was engulfed by flames, causing an estimated £2.25m of damage. Caused by a lightning bolt it destroyed the roof and saw over 150 fire-fighters tackle the blaze for well over two hours.**

In the garden

Natural weed killers

If you've got dogs or cats walking round in your garden, using chemical-filled weed killer can be extremely harmful to them. There are many other ways of killing your weeds using chemical-free alternatives such as vinegar for paving and driveways, salt-water, boiling-hot water and even baking soda to destroy growing weeds.

I never knew that!

During Wimbledon around 53,000 tennis balls are used. They're replaced after every seventh to ninth game and are stored very specifically at 20°C/68F to ensure they're in match-fit condition! Slazenger has been Wimbledon's official tennis ball supplier since 1902, making it one of the longest partnerships in sporting history.

Wonderful wildlife on your doorstep!

PIC: ALAMY STOCK PHOTO

NAME: **Weasel**

HABITAT: **Wide ranging from grasslands to moors and woodland.**

DIET: **Voles, mice, birds, eggs and even rabbits.**

FAST FACT: **A super-quick metabolism means that weasels need to eat around one third of their body weight per day to survive.**

Recipe of the week

NEW POTATO SALAD WITH ASPARAGUS AND BLUE CHEESE

SERVES: 4 PREP: 20 MINS COOK: 5 MINS

500g (1lb 2oz) asparagus spears
Juice of 1 lemon
1 tbsp olive oil
Sea salt and black pepper, to season
250g (9oz) New/Baby potatoes, boiled and cut into quarters lengthwise
250g (9oz) cherry tomatoes
50g (2oz) black olives, stoned and halved
2 small shallots, finely chopped
1 tbsp basil, finely chopped
150g (5oz) crumbly blue cheese, crumbled or cut into 1cm cubes

1 Clean and trim the asparagus, then add to a pan of boiling salted water. Blanch for 1-3 mins until tender.
2 Remove the asparagus from the pan and rinse in cold water to prevent further cooking.
3 Mix the lemon juice, olive oil, salt and pepper together for the dressing.
4 In a large bowl, toss together the boiled potatoes, tomatoes, olives, shallots and basil with the dressing.
5 Lay out the asparagus in a serving dish, spoon the potato mix onto the asparagus then top with the blue cheese.
www.seasonalspuds.com

12 SUNDAY

13 MONDAY

14 TUESDAY

15 WEDNESDAY

16 THURSDAY

17 FRIDAY

18 SATURDAY

A magical memory

A KENYAN SAFARI

I was 33 and had just got divorced when I went abroad for the first time in 1984. I loved wildlife so I decided to treat myself to a safari in Kenya.

The nine-hour flight was frightening and exhilarating at the same time as I was on my own and had never been in an aircraft before. I wasn't prepared for the surge of the engines on take-off, the noise during the flight or the power of the brakes on landing.

On arrival at a hotel in Nairobi, I met my fellow travellers for the start of our great adventure. We travelled 1,000 miles in a week. I remember the dry heat of the savannah, the beautiful bird song and the excitement of spotting the 'big five' as we bumped over the dirt tracks. We were covered in dust at the end of each day but it didn't matter as we were able to freshen up when we arrived at our comfortable lodges for the night where we were given plenty of tasty food, fresh tropical fruit and copious amounts of liquid refreshment.

The highlights included seeing a cheetah close up and crossing the Equator.
Chris Barrow via email

On this week

JULY 16, 1969: **The first attempt to land a man on the moon takes off from Cape Kennedy Florida in Apollo 11. Sure enough, a few months later the man in that rocket – Neil Armstrong – made history by taking the first footsteps on the moon's surface.**

In the garden

Keeping your fruit safe

If you're growing fruit in your garden, such as strawberries, raspberries or blackberries, you'll need to protect them from birds or slugs. The easiest way to do this is with anti-bird netting. It can be moulded and changed in shape to protect your fruit no matter where it's located in the garden using poles of bamboo and cable ties to form the cage.

I never knew that!

Dorothy's famous ruby slippers in the 1939 film The Wizard of Oz, were originally silver - just like in the original novel by L Frank Baum. However, when it came to filming, studio bosses decided that red was a better choice to show off the new Technicolor film process.

Wonderful wildlife on your doorstep!

PIC: ALAMY STOCK PHOTO

NAME: **Common or smooth newt**
HABITAT: **Wetland, bogs, marshes and ponds throughout the UK.**
DIET: **Insects, caterpillars, worms as well as water crustaceans and even tadpoles.**
FAST FACT: **In the breeding season the males develop a wavy transparent crest from their head to their tail.**

Recipe of the week

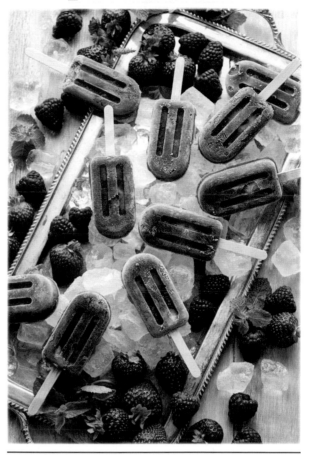

STRAWBERRY, RASPBERRY AND PIMM'S LOLLIES

SERVES: 8 PREP: 10 MINS FREEZE: 4 HOURS

300g (10 ½ oz) strawberries and raspberries
Leaves from 1 stem of mint
50g (2oz) icing sugar
100ml (4 fl oz) Pimm's
200ml (7 fl oz) lemonade
4 slices cucumber, quartered
4 strawberries, sliced

1 Put the berries, mint leaves and icing sugar into a blender and whizz until smooth. Pour through a fine sieve to remove the seeds.
2 Combine the berry mixture with the Pimm's and lemonade and stir well. Put the cucumber and strawberry slices into lolly moulds and pour in the liquid.
3 Freeze for 4 hours or until solid.
Berryworld

19 SUNDAY

20 MONDAY

21 TUESDAY

22 WEDNESDAY

23 THURSDAY

24 FRIDAY

25 SATURDAY

A magical memory

HAIR TODAY, GONE TOMORROW

Meet my elegant doll, Jane, who came into my life when I was three years old. She thrilled me by being just a tad shorter than I was at the time.

Jane was a present from my Nanna and she had beautiful chestnut brown curls - until one day when Mum took me to the hairdresser's. Thinking I'd copy the hairdresser's talents, I picked up my scissors and massacred her lovely locks. Sadly, I didn't realise that, unlike my hair, her curls would never grow again. Jane spent the next fifty years confined to a shelf in the spare room dressed either in a winter coat and hat that Mum made for her or in a summer dress and Fifties-style headscarf to hide her embarrassment. Aside from her lack of hair, my clumsy fingers had knocked her eye askew, leaving her with an unfortunate squint.

Last year my sister and her husband decided to take Jane in hand. As well as gluing her eyes straight and restoring her beautiful lashes, they fashioned a hairpiece in a funky style and gave her a new dress.

No longer hidden away, Jane now resides in a chair in our sunny conservatory.
Virginia Leverton via email

On this week

JULY 23, 1986: **Prince Andrew married Sarah Ferguson in front of a worldwide TV audience of more than 500 million. Their first kiss as man and wife on the balcony of Buckingham Palace prompted roars from the crowds watching below.**

In the garden

Ways to save water

We use plenty of water to cook with, such as the water we use to boil pasta, potatoes or veg. This water is full of nutrients that could benefit your plants so rather than pouring it down the sink, save it in a jug or bottle to fully cool down before using it to quench the thirst of your plants when watering.

I never knew that!

Every year in Northern California a World Dog Surfing Championship is held. Canine competitors battle it out in different surfing heats, or if doggy paddle isn't their strong stroke they can take part in frisbee and ball catching competitions! These pampered pooches also enjoy a wellness fair with massages and health check-ups.

Wonderful wildlife on your doorstep!

C. ALAMY
STOCK PHOTO

NAME: **Moorhen**
HABITAT: **River, lakes and wetlands across the UK.**
DIET: **Small fish, insects as well as berries, leaves and seeds.**
FAST FACT: **The name 'Moorhen' is quite misleading as this is a wetland bird, but the moor part of its name is an old expression of marsh, simply meaning bird of the marshes.**

Recipe of the week

BLUE CHEESE BEEF BURGER WITH CELERY AND RADISH SALSA

SERVES: 4 PREP: 10 MINS COOK: 20 MINS

For the shallots:
8 shallots
3 tsp butter
1 tsp brown sugar
½ tsp balsamic vinegar
For the salsa:
4 radishes
2 sticks celery
½ tbsp white wine vinegar
½ tbsp olive oil
For the burger:
4 beef burgers
4 brioche burger buns
1 little gem lettuce
4 slices of blue cheese

1 Peel and slice the shallots. Heat the butter in a pan, add the sugar and vinegar and swirl together.
2 Add the shallots, season and stir to coat. Cook until caramel coloured and soft. Set aside.
3 Make the salsa. Finely dice the radish and celery, put them in a bowl with the oil and vinegar and season. Stir well and set aside.
4 Cook the burgers on the barbecue or griddle and toast the buns. Layer with little gem on the base of the bun then the salsa. Put the burger on top with a slice of cheese, then top with the caramelised shallots. Hold the whole thing together with a skewer or steak knife through the middle.
Loveradish.co.uk

26 SUNDAY

27 MONDAY

28 TUESDAY

29 WEDNESDAY

30 THURSDAY

31 FRIDAY

1 SATURDAY

A magical memory

HOLIDAY DISASTER

This is me, aged sixteen, with my schoolfriend, Margaret, on holiday at Land's End. I am on the right in a white cardigan. It was the first time I had been allowed to take a friend with me as the year before I had been so lonely and bored on my own it was decided I could have a friend for company.

My parents had booked a chalet in the middle of nowhere with no bus route nearby and the nearest beach was three miles away. To get there, we had to walk, carrying all our beach gear. We decided we needed to find someone with a car to ferry us about. When we met two boys a little bit older than us with a nice car our adventures began - much to my parents' horror.

It was a disaster from start to finish as my mum and dad never knew where we were and with no mobile phones to keep them informed of our whereabouts it was a constant worry for them. So that was the last time I was allowed to take a friend on holiday with me!
Christine Davies, Wadebridge

On this week

JULY 30, 1991: **The Italian tenor Luciano Pavarotti celebrates 30 years in opera with a huge free concert in London's Hyde Park that sees him belt out arias from Verdi, Puccini and Wagner in the pouring British rain.**

In the garden

Save money, save the world!

By making your own compost, you're not only reducing the amount of landfill waste you produce and saving money, but it will also maintain a healthy garden. You can use just about any degradable waste in your compost bin, from leaves and weeds in the garden, vacuum cleaner dust and hair from brushes from the house and also any food waste from the kitchen.

I never knew that!

The hugely popular Shake 'n' Vac advert, where actress Jenny Logan danced around vacuuming the living room in her high heels, ran for six years from 1980 to 1986! So popular was the advert with its catchy tune, that it was even voted TV's most popular jingle.

Wonderful wildlife on your doorstep!

PIC: ALAMY STOCK PHOTO

NAME: **Common dolphin**
HABITAT: **Found in deep waters off the coast of Cornwall, particularly near Padstow.**
DIET: **Fish including herring, cod and mackerel, but will also eat squid.**
FAST FACT: **Dolphins each develop their own unique whistle, which other dolphins can use to identify them.**

Recipe of the week

MANGO AND LIME SORBET

SERVES: 4 PREP: 10 MINS COOK: NONE

500g (1lb 2oz) frozen mango chunks
1 lime, zest and juice
100ml (4fl oz) coconut water
1 tbsp caster sugar (optional)
200g (7oz) fresh raspberries
100g (4oz) coconut shavings
Fresh mint to garnish

1 Place half of the mango into the bowl of a food processor and add the juice and zest of the lime. Begin to process the mango and juice and gradually add a little coconut water until you form the sorbet.
2 Taste, and add a little sugar if you wish.
3 Gradually add more mango and coconut water until you achieve the right consistency.
4 Place a few raspberries in the bottom of a tall glass and spoon the mango sorbet on top. Decorate with more raspberries, shaved coconut and fresh mint.
Love your gut

2 SUNDAY

3 MONDAY

4 TUESDAY

5 WEDNESDAY

6 THURSDAY

7 FRIDAY

8 SATURDAY

A magical memory

BELOVED DOLLY

Of all the toys I had as a child, none could rival my doll, Margaret. There was a dolly with no name that had been handed down to me by my sister, a small blue teddy who smelled of disinfectant after I had been sick on him, a knitted panda and a really lovely doll who cried 'Mama', but Margaret was my favourite.

She was a present from my godmother and had a sweet painted face with rosy cheeks, blue eyes and a tiny smile. One day when I jumped out of bed, I landed on Margaret's head and after that she had a large crack running from her forehead to her chin, but I still loved her. She was hugged so much that the fur on her onesie was worn away so Mum made her a smart two-piece suit with pink stitching, a pocket and a matching hanky.

The photo is of me in the garden with my twin brother, Dennis, but I'm afraid the dolly peeping over the side of the pram is not Margaret.
Diana Mansell, Grantham

On this week

AUGUST 5, 1962: **Screen siren Marilyn Monroe is found dead in her bed in Los Angeles. Her death came after months of concerning behaviour where she'd been fired by Fox for repeatedly not turning up to the filming of Something's Got To Give.**

In the garden
Edible nettles

Why not bring some stinging nettles inside and enjoy them with dinner? With a little exposure to heat, the nettles will lose their sting and will taste similar to spinach. All you need to do is wash them by dunking them into a bowl of boiling hot salt water before cooking over a high heat with butter or oil and seasoning with salt.

I never knew that!

Nowhere in England is more than 80 miles from the sea and what a coastline we boast. According to the Ordnance Survey the Great British coastline is around 11,072 miles (17,820 km) long, making it one of the longest coastlines in Europe.

Wonderful wildlife on your doorstep!

PIC: ALAMY STOCK PHOTO

NAME: **Kingfisher**
HABITAT: **Rivers and streams across the UK.**
DIET: **Fish including minnows and sticklebacks and also insects and tadpoles.**
FAST FACT: **To attract female kingfishers, the male will try to feed her a fish. If she refuses he'll simply eat it and then try another female!**

Recipe of the week

BARBECUE SHALLOT AND LAMB FLATBREADS

SERVES: 6 PREP: 15 MINS + MARINATING COOK: 10 MINS

600g (1lb 5oz) lamb leg steaks, cut into bite-sized pieces
2 tbsp olive oil
1 lemon, zest and juice
3 cloves garlic, crushed
2 tsp dried oregano
6 shallots, peeled and quartered through the root
Salt and freshly ground black pepper
To serve:
6 flatbreads, wraps
or pitta bread
Tub of tzatziki
Slices of tomato
and cucumber

1 In a bowl mix the lamb, olive oil, lemon zest and juice, garlic and oregano. Season, stir and cover with cling film. Leave to marinate in the fridge for a couple of hours.
2 Heat the barbecue or grill.
3 Thread the lamb and shallot quarters onto the skewers and grill for about 8-9 mins, turning occasionally.
4 Warm the flatbreads or pittas by wrapping them in foil and laying on the grill.
5 Serve with tzatziki and a cucumber and tomato salad.
www.ukshallot.com

9 SUNDAY

10 MONDAY

11 TUESDAY

12 WEDNESDAY

13 THURSDAY

14 FRIDAY

15 SATURDAY

A magical memory

DAMP BUT HAPPY CAMPERS

I am the second girl on the right in this photo taken when I went camping with the Girl Guides. After arriving at a field and setting up bell tents that slept three people, we proceeded to dig a trench for the latrine, discreetly surrounded by sacking. That was the toilet done!

Next we were each given a large sack full of straw. Those were our mattresses (or palliases). We were a little peeved to discover the Guide mistress had her own tent and a camp bed. We cleaned our teeth daily, but as the water was cold not many of us washed!

It rained every day, but that didn't stop us from enjoying ourselves. We played rounders and sang around the camp fire. One day we had a competition to see which group could cook the best breakfast. Our group came second from last as the bacon was burned and the eggs over cooked, but we ate it as if it was the best meal ever!

We had a good adventure but weren't sorry to get home and have a good night's sleep in our own beds.

Anne Clarke, Somerset

On this week

15-18 AUGUST, 1969: **The world's largest rock festival, Woodstock, took place in a dairy farm in the Catskill Mountains, northwest of New York. Among the musicians to perform to the crowds of 400,000 were Jimi Hendrix, Janis Joplin and The Who.**

In the garden

Stay in shape

Gardening isn't always an easy task and it can take a lot of strength and energy to keep on top of your patch. That's why it's important to invest in a good pair of knee-pads and top-quality tools to make light work of jobs. It's also a good idea to do some stretches after you've been out and about and make sure you're moisturising your skin regularly.

I never knew that!

The highest ever summer temperature across the UK was 38.5°C, recorded on 10th August 2003 in Faversham, Kent. The year 2018 was another sizzler with heatwave temperatures reaching 35.3°C, but for longevity the summer of 1976 brought us temperatures exceeding a scorching 32°C for two weeks in July.

Wonderful wildlife on your doorstep!

PIC: ALAMY
STOCK PHOTO

NAME: **Slow worm**
HABITAT: **Grassland, heathland, woodland edges and gardens.**
DIET: **Slugs, worms, snails and insects.**
FAST FACT: **The slow worm is actually a legless lizard and not a worm or snake! Often found in gardens, you're unlikely to see them if you have a cat as they make a tasty snack.**

Recipe of the week

STRAWBERRY & LIME MARZIPAN CROUTES

SERVES: 6 PREP: 15 MINS COOK: 25 MINS

6 slices brioche or use brioche buns and slice open
175g (6oz) marzipan, grated
300g (10½ oz) strawberries, hulled and sliced
1 lime, halved
Sprinkle of sugar (optional)
Handful of flaked almonds
Icing sugar to dust
Crème fraîche or Greek yogurt to serve (optional)

1 Preheat the oven to 190°C/375°F/Gas Mark 5. Sit the brioche on a baking sheet then evenly scatter over the marzipan.
2 Divide the strawberries between each one then squeeze over the lime juice then sprinkle with sugar if using and almonds.
3 Put in the oven to toast for about 20-25 mins or until the brioche is golden and the topping is bubbling.
4. Remove and dust with icing sugar and serve with a dollop of crème fraîche or Greek yogurt.

www.jubileestrawberries.co.uk

16 SUNDAY

17 MONDAY

18 TUESDAY

19 WEDNESDAY

20 THURSDAY

21 FRIDAY

22 SATURDAY

A magical memory

ON THE ROAD AGAIN

I was born in America and my love of travel was inspired by our family's summer holidays when my parents used to drive from our home in Tacoma, Washington to visit my mother's relatives in San Pedro, California. Every year our horizons were widened by these two-week forays.

This was back in the Forties so we didn't jet our way to our destinations - the open road beckoned and we piled into the family Chevrolet. In-car entertainment was limited to the radio but the reception ebbed and flowed as we progressed from town to town. We stayed in motels that had names such as Sleep Awhile and Rest Well. Their amenities included a washcloth and soap. Our parents would make a spot decision as to a motel's fitness. "Fourteen dollars!" bellowed our father in front of a Las Vegas property. "That's too much." And we drove on.

Among the many places we visited were Salt Lake City, Yellowstone Park and the Alamo. The photo was taken of me with my brother John and our mother, Madeleine, at the Grand Canyon in Arizona.
Wynne Crombie, via email

On this week

AUGUST 15, 1959: **The Morris Mini car - an icon of British culture and the swinging Sixties - was launched when the head of the British Motor Corporation said he wanted to create a 'proper miniature car' that would rival the increasingly-popular Bubble Car.**

In the garden
Organic fertiliser
There are so many ingredients lurking in your cupboards that could make fantastic fertiliser. Banana skins, green tea and even matches can be buried in the ground alongside your plants. These household objects will work as an effective fertiliser to your plants providing them with vital nutrients to thrive.

I never knew that!

The Queen served as a truck mechanic in the Women's Auxiliary Territorial Service during the Second World War. Based in Camberley, Surrey, the young Princess Elizabeth learnt to drive as well as to change a wheel and even rebuild an engine!

Wonderful wildlife on your doorstep!

PIC: ALAMY STOCK PHOTO

NAME: **Swallowtail butterfly**
HABITAT: **Wetland and marshes, currently only found on the Norfolk Broads.**
DIET: **Milk parsley as caterpillars, adult butterflies feed on any type of flower.**
FAST FACT: **Swallowtail butterfly caterpillars have a unique horn-like organ called an osmeterium which excretes a scent to deter predators.**

Recipe of the week

VEGGIE CLUB SANDWICH

SERVES: 1 PREP: 10 MINS

75g (3oz) kale
2 tsp French dressing
3 slices bread, toasted
50g (2oz) coleslaw
50g (2oz) hummus
25g (2oz) Cheddar cheese, grated

1 Cook the kale in boiling water for 4 mins, drain and run under cold water. Remove any thick stalks and squeeze out excess liquid. Mix with the dressing and place on top of 1 slice of toast. Top this with coleslaw.
2 Spread another slice of toast with houmous and sprinkle over the cheese, place on top of the coleslaw. Top with the remaining slice of toast and cut in half. Serve with a few crisps and a handful of salad.
www.waitrose.com/recipes

23 SUNDAY

24 MONDAY

25 TUESDAY

26 WEDNESDAY

27 THURSDAY

28 FRIDAY

29 SATURDAY

A magical memory

A SUMMER WEDDING

Bill and I met at a local youth club and married two years later in 1966. This is my favourite photo of us, turning round as if to look at our past before turning to walk into our future together. Our wedding was in August and I had a beautiful bouquet of pink carnations while our bridesmaids carried baskets of sweet peas.

The reception was in a café in Brighouse over a clothing and lingerie shop that no longer exists. We had a turkey salad for our wedding breakfast and the quietest guest was Auntie Dorothy's poodle, Kim, who sat on a piano stool by the table – even though my mum had asked her not to bring him.

We were going to go to Skegness for our honeymoon but changed our minds as Bill only had a couple of days' holiday from the farm where he worked. It was just as well as the car we were planning to go in broke down when his family went home in it! We have now been married for fifty-four years and have two sons and six grandchildren.

Pat Mason, via email

On this week

AUGUST 24, 1967: **Today's scorching temperature of over 27°C was too much for most people to bear but especially so for two penguins from Chessington Zoo who were taken on a day trip to a local ice-rink to try to cool off from the heat.**

In the garden

DIY garden furniture

You can make some stylish garden furniture out of just about anything. Old shelves can be attached to garden walls or fences to display small plant pots while old ladders can be used for plants such as sweet peas to climb up. You could even upcycle household furniture to create small outdoor tables or stools.

I never knew that!

The shortest war in history was the Anglo-Zanzibar War, which lasted around 38 minutes. The conflict between the UK and the Zanzibar Sultanate took place on August 27th 1896. The casualty rate for such a short effort was high, with 500 of the opposition's fighters killed or injured. Just one British officer was injured.

Wonderful wildlife on your doorstep!

PIC: ALAMY STOCK PHOTO

NAME: **Roe deer**
HABITAT: **Widespread in woodland across Scotland and some parts of England.**
DIET: **Brambles, hedgerows, crops, tree leaves, flowers, fruit, nuts, heather and grasses.**
FAST FACT: **Roe deer, like red deer, are indigenous to Britain and were re-introduced after being hunted to extinction during the 18th Century.**

Recipe of the week

MOROCCAN BEEF-STUFFED TOMATOES

SERVES: 4 PREP: 5 MINS COOK: 25 MINS

1 onion, chopped
400g (14oz) pack lean minced beef
1 tbsp ras el hanout seasoning
8 large tomatoes
1 beef stock cube
250g (9oz) pouch spelt, quinoa, red rice & wild rice

1 Preheat the oven to 200°C/400°F/Gas Mark 6. Fry the onion, minced beef and seasoning in a saucepan to brown.
2 Meanwhile, cut the tops off the tomatoes and scoop out the flesh, leaving a 1cm (1/2 in) border around the edges, and place on a baking tray.
3 Add the tomato pulp to the minced beef with the stock cube and cook for 15 mins. Stir in the grains and season to taste.
4 Fill the tomatoes with the mince and bake for 10 mins until just soft. Serve sprinkled with parsley and a fresh side salad.
www.waitrose.com/recipes

30 SUNDAY

31 MONDAY

1 TUESDAY

2 WEDNESDAY

3 THURSDAY

4 FRIDAY

5 SATURDAY

A magical memory

BLACKPOOL WAS BLISS

Here is a picture taken on our annual family holiday in Blackpool. We are outside the amusement arcade and I think we were still chuckling after Mum put money in the slot machine to hear the Laughing Policeman.

Aged sixteen, I am wearing the latest fashion. I had borrowed my mum's shoes which were pink leather with silver heels and wooden soles. I felt very grown up. The other two in the photo are my younger sister and brother. My older brother was away doing his National Service.

We saved for the whole year ready for going away and we certainly had a good time. We stayed in a boarding house which had a wireless in every room and provided three meals a day. The landlady boasted that it had a sea view, but my mum said we would need binoculars to see it. Dad used to sit on the beach in his overcoat even though it was hot and sunny.

We were a close, happy family and I always loved and cared for my younger siblings.
Angela Patchett, Fleetwood

On this week

SEPTEMBER 1, 1976: **After weeks of sun, the drought worsens as the first of 11,500 standpipes are connected in Yorkshire. The drought dragged on for weeks but little did anyone realise all they needed to do was appoint a Minister for Drought, Dennis Howell, to make it rain again.**

In the garden

Good seed or bad seed?

It's important to test seeds to check if they are good to plant. Take a damp paper towel and place 3-4 seeds in the paper towel and place in a warm spot in your house. Lay it on top of the clothes dryer or on a heating pad set on very low. If you don't see any sprouts within a couple days, they're not viable for planting anymore.

I never knew that!

The grey tabby cat which sits on Marlon Brando's lap during the iconic opening scene of The Godfather (1972), wasn't actually part of the script. In fact, the presumed stray kitty was wandering around the studio when director Francis Ford Coppola placed it in Marlon's arms and the pair immediately bonded.

Wonderful wildlife on your doorstep!

PIC: ALAMY
STOCK PHOTO

NAME: **Bumblebee**
HABITAT: **Gardens, orchards and parks throughout the UK.**
DIET: **Pollen and nectar.**
FAST FACT: **There are 25 recorded species of bumblebee in the UK, although only around six are commonly seen in our gardens including the yellow and black striped garden bumblebee.**

Recipe of the week

LEMON COD WITH ROASTED VEG

SERVES: 2 PREP: 10 MINS COOK: 25 MINS

400g (14oz) pack Mediterranean roasting vegetables
Zest and juice of 1 lemon
2 tsp wholegrain mustard
260g (9oz) pack skinless & boneless cod fillets

1 Preheat the oven to 200°C/400F/Gas Mark 6. Place the vegetables in a small roasting tray. Drizzle over half the lemon zest and juice and bake for 10 mins.
2 Meanwhile, mix the remaining lemon zest and juice with the mustard.
3 Place the cod on top of the vegetables and spread over the mustard mixture. Bake for a further 15 mins or until the cod is just cooked. Serve with steamed baby new potatoes.
www.waitrose.com/recipes

6 SUNDAY

7 MONDAY

8 TUESDAY

9 WEDNESDAY

10 THURSDAY

11 FRIDAY

12 SATURDAY

A magical memory

NOT GOOD VIBRATIONS

My pop idols were The Beach Boys. My two friends and I read in a newspaper article that they were staying at the Hilton hotel in London so we decided to get on the tube to see if we could catch a glimpse of them.

When we arrived we saw them sitting on a balcony, seven floors up. We waved at them and they waved back. We were so excited we decided to see if we could find their rooms. We went into the hotel and took the lift up to the seventh floor. We guessed which room it must be and knocked on the door. Unfortunately, it was not one of The Beach Boys but an older woman who did not look very happy. We tried several other rooms with no luck.

All of a sudden, two members of staff grabbed us and gave us a right ticking off. They told us if we came into the hotel again, they would call the police. We had to get on the tube and go home. We never told our mums - they would have gone mad at us.

Christine Markham, via email

On this week

SEPTEMBER 10, 1973: **Designer Barbara Hulanicki re-opened the doors of her iconic Biba department store in Kensington after a £1m refurbishment. Stocking not just clothes, but cosmetics, household goods and even a food hall, her Art Deco designs became must-haves in every Seventies home.**

In the garden

Toilet paper rolls

Don't throw away old cardboard toilet paper rolls, they come in very handy for sowing seeds. Many veggie seeds like peas don't like their roots to be disturbed early on so it's a good idea to put them in toilet roll seedling pots. Once the plant begins to grow you can plant them straight in the ground with the roll as this will disintegrate into the ground.

I never knew that!

Every day around eight million pieces of plastic enter our oceans and closer to home for every mile of UK beaches, 150 plastic bottles are found littering them. Sadly, each plastic bottle could potentially survive intact for 450 years in the sea.

Wonderful wildlife on your doorstep!

PIC: ALAMY STOCK PHOTO

NAME: **Otter**

HABITAT: **Semi-aquatic, otters can be found in rivers, wetlands and marshes mostly in northern and western England.**

DIET: **Fish, eels, salmonids and frogs.**

LIFESPAN: **5-10 years.**

FAST FACT: **In the Fifties and Sixties, pesticide pollution meant that otter population disappeared completely from much of England. Now a protected species, otter numbers are gradually on the rise.**

Recipe of the week

BLUEBERRY AND BREAD PUDDING

SERVES: 4 PREP: 20 MINS + RESTING TIME COOK: 35 MINS

8 slices white bread
4 tbsp lemon curd
150g (5oz) blueberries
3 eggs
150ml (¼pt) milk
150ml (¼pt) double cream
50g (2oz) caster sugar, plus a little extra for sprinkling
25g (1oz) butter, melted

1 Preheat the oven to 180°C/350°F/Gas Mark 4. Spread half the bread slices with lemon curd then cover with the remaining slices. Trim off the crusts then cut each sandwich into 8 cubes. Add to a 1.2 litre (2pt) buttered, shallow, ovenproof dish and scatter with the blueberries.
2 Whisk the eggs, milk and cream with the sugar then pour over the bread and leave to soak for 20 mins.
3 Drizzle with the melted butter and sprinkle with a little extra sugar and bake for 30-35 mins until the bread is golden and the custard just set. Scoop into bowls and serve warm with a drizzle of cream.

www.seasonalberries.co.uk

13 SUNDAY

14 MONDAY

15 TUESDAY

16 WEDNESDAY

17 THURSDAY

18 FRIDAY

19 SATURDAY

A magical memory

SECOND TIME AROUND

This photo was taken in Thailand when Den and I were on honeymoon. We were visiting the island where The Golden Gun was filmed and we were trying to do a James Bond pose. As you can see, I couldn't get it right and everyone was laughing including the Chinese gentleman who was taking the picture.

I found love second time around. I had been divorced for some years when I started going to a dance class with the girls from work. One evening while I was at the bar a stranger spoke to me. He told me he had lost his wife and his friends had invited him out. He asked if he could ask me to dance in the practice interval.

After that Den and I bumped into each other quite often. When his work brought him up north he asked if he could stay at my place as he'd been told he was going to do nightshifts. In the end, the nightshifts never happened but Den stayed at mine anyway and many months later he proposed.

While we were in Bangkok we had our marriage blessed by monks.
Chris Matthewman, via email

On this week

SEPTEMBER 16, 1968: **For the first time the Post Office operates a two-tier postal system. Many people queued up round the block to buy the first 5d first-class stamps while others complained the new system was too confusing and made sending letters too difficult.**

In the garden

Our buzzing friends

Bees play a vital role in our ecosystem so it's terribly important we do our bit to look out for them. Make sure you have plenty of nectar-rich plants about that bloom year round while letting your grass grow to give them much-needed shelter. Put out a shallow saucer of water with a pebble in the centre for them to rest on while they drink.

I never knew that!

There are more miles of canal in Birmingham than in Venice. In fact Birmingham has an impressive 35 miles, while Venice only has 26 miles. There are also more than 400 bridges in Venice.

Wonderful wildlife on your doorstep!

PIC: SHUTTERSTOCK

NAME: **Minke Whale**
HABITAT: **Around the UK they can be seen in the Atlantic Ocean and the northern North Sea.**
DIET: **Fish and plankton.**
FAST FACT: **Minke whales gulp feed, which means they take large gulps of fish and the seawater is pushed out through baleen plates that line their mouths.**

Recipe of the week

LEEK WITH MUSTARD AND MASCARPONE ON GARLIC TOAST

SERVES: 4 PREP: 10 MIN COOK: 15 MINS

30g (1oz) unsalted butter
2 medium leeks, trimmed, washed, cut in half lengthways and cut into half-moons
100ml (4fl oz) whipping cream
150g (5oz) mascarpone cheese (or goat's cheese)
Twist of milled pepper
2 tbsp of parsley, finely chopped
1 tsp of Tewkesbury mustard (optional)
4 slices of crusty bread
1 peeled clove garlic

1 Melt the butter in a saucepan on a gentle heat and then add the leeks. Simmer gently for 5 mins until the leeks are tender then turn the heat up slightly to reduce any moisture in the pan.
2 Turn the heat down again and add the cream. Boil for about 1 min - or until the mixture looks nice and thick.
3 Add the mascarpone or goat's cheese and beat it well into the mixture until melted and bound together. Season with pepper, parsley and the mustard.
4 Toast the bread. Then rub the slices with the garlic, place the leeks on top and serve. You can glaze this mixture under the grill until golden and to gain a better glaze beat a fresh egg yolk into the mix before glazing.
www.british-leeks.co.uk

20 SUNDAY

21 MONDAY

22 TUESDAY

23 WEDNESDAY

24 THURSDAY

25 FRIDAY

26 SATURDAY

A magical memory

SAUSAGES AND BEANS

I spent many happy hours with both the Brownies and the Guides. In the Brownies, I was in the Fairies and at each meeting we held hands and danced around the toadstool singing, 'We are the fairies, bright and gay, helping others every day'. Each Six had a different song to sing.

When I moved on to the Guides, I enjoyed going to camp. We did things that would never be allowed today. For a start, we travelled there in the back of an open lorry, sitting on our kit bags. Seat belts were not even thought of. Our tents were very basic with only groundsheets – I once found I had been sleeping on an ants' nest and was covered in bites. The campfire was a wigwam of sticks with a billycan hanging from the top to heat water. Sausages were cooked on the end of sticks held into the fire. We did finally graduate to using an old frying pan in which we cooked baked beans as well.

This photo is of me with my brother Barry in his cub scout's uniform.
Annie Chambers, Wimborne

On this week

SEPTEMBER 22, 1955: **For the first time we could choose the channel on our tellies as Britain's first independent television station came on air, ending the BBC's 18-year monopoly on the airwaves and introducing us to our first-ever TV advertisements.**

In the garden

Leaf compost

It won't be long now until the leaves start falling from the trees and it's simple to turn these leaves into compost. Just pop them all into a plastic bag or bin liner with some holes in the bottom for drainage and leave in the garden. Over the next few months and years the leaves will gradually turn into the perfect compost.

I never knew that!

Mongolian emperor Genghis Khan didn't allow paintings, sculptures or engravings of his appearance, so any we see today were created after his death. He also requested that he be buried in an unmarked burial site and even today there is a memorial site, but no official grave.

Wonderful wildlife on your doorstep!

PIC: ALAMY STOCK PHOTO

NAME: **Barn Owl**
HABITAT: **Mostly grass and farmland.**
DIET: **Voles, shrews and mice – often swallowed whole.**
FAST FACT: **While the Barn Owl's super-soft feathers help them fly almost silently, they're not waterproof, so they avoid hunting in wet weather.**

Recipe of the week

ROASTED SQUASH AND CHICKPEA SOUP

SERVES: 4 PREP: 15 MINS COOK: 30 MINS

500g (1lb 2oz) butternut squash (cut into large pieces)
Pinch of chilli flakes
1 tbsp olive oil
400ml (14fl oz) can reduced-fat coconut milk
500ml (1pt) vegetable stock
400g (14oz) can of drained chickpeas
25g (1oz) toasted pumpkin seeds

1 Preheat the oven to 200°C/400°F/Gas Mark 6.
2 Place the squash on a baking tray with a pinch of chilli flakes and toss in 1 tbsp olive oil. Roast for 20-25 mins.
3 Meanwhile, add the coconut milk, vegetable stock and the chickpeas, add the squash, cover and simmer for 5 mins.
4 Blend with a stick blender to smooth. Sprinkle with pumpkin seeds and serve with crusty bread.

www.waitrose.com/recipes

27 SUNDAY

28 MONDAY

29 TUESDAY

30 WEDNESDAY

1 THURSDAY

2 FRIDAY

3 SATURDAY

A magical memory

GRAMMAR SCHOOL GIRL

This is me in my parents' back garden, ready for my first day at grammar school. I was wearing my brand-new navy blue uniform and my satchel was the one my dad had carried as a schoolboy. I felt like a bride with something old and something new.

Some months earlier I'd heard one of my junior school teachers say to another teacher: "Give me the boys for a year and I'll get them through the 11-plus. Girls are no good." I was consumed with fury. This was the man who sat with his feet up on the desk, reading a newspaper, while his class of eight-year-olds ran riot around him.

That overheard conversation ignited a spark in me. I would show him what girls could do. Fortunately, I was in a class nurtured by a lovely teacher who brought out the best in all of us. As a result, I was one of the first girls in the history of our school to pass the 11-plus exam. There's nothing girls can't do just as well as boys.

Mary Cook, Gainsborough

On this week

OCTOBER 3, 1961: **One of our favourite actors Dick Van Dyke launched his very own sitcom on American television called the Dick Van Dyke Show. Created by comedian Carl Reiner it starred the likes of Mary Tyler Moore, Rose Marie and Morey Amsterdam.**

In the garden

Clever coffee

Use your coffee grounds to keep slugs away from plants. If you don't grind your own coffee beans, your local coffee shop might give you some for free if you ask. The coffee grounds are great to use around hostas as slugs particularly love these and they'll devour them if undeterred.

I never knew that!

After the sun, the closest star to Earth is Proxima Centauri, which is about 4.22 light years away. In 2016 astronomers discovered that the star has a planet slightly bigger than ours orbiting it, although scientists believe it's unlikely that Proxima b, as it's called, could support any life form.

Wonderful wildlife on your doorstep!

PIC: ALAMY STOCK PHOTO

NAME: **Grey Seal**
HABITAT: **Mainly the UK's northern and western coastlines.**
DIET: **White fish, sand eels and flat fish.**
FAST FACT: **Grey seal pups are born with thick white fur. Within a few weeks they triple their body mass, building a layer of blubber to keep them warm.**

Recipe of the week

BRAMLEY BAP WITH AMARETTO CHERRY

SERVES: 1 PREP: 5 MINS COOK: 30 MINS

1 Bramley apple
Knob of softened butter
1 tsp brown sugar
6 black cherries in syrup
2 amaretto biscuits, crushed
Splash of amaretto
Vanilla ice-cream, to serve

1 Preheat oven to 180°C/350°F/Gas Mark 4.
2 Score the circumference of the apple with a sharp knife. Scoop out the core and a little of the flesh to make room for the filling.
3 Spread the butter into the middle of the apple and sprinkle with brown sugar. Mix cherries with crushed amaretto biscuits and stuff into the apple middle. Add a splash of amaretto.
4 Place apple in a baking dish, put the apple top back on and bake for 25-30 minutes or until soft and tinged golden brown

Optional: add 1 tbsp sugar to the syrup from the cherries and reduce this down to a sticky sauce over a medium heat in a small saucepan and use to drizzle over the apple. Serve with a scoop of vanilla ice-cream.
Bramley Apples

4 SUNDAY

5 MONDAY

6 TUESDAY

7 WEDNESDAY

8 THURSDAY

9 FRIDAY

10 SATURDAY

A magical memory

GRAMPY AND GAL

My grandfather, or Grampy as I always called him, was a central force in my life until his death when I was aged thirteen. My grandmother had died two years before I was born so Grampy lived with my parents and when I arrived he felt God had sent me to give him a reason for living without his beloved wife.

As both my parents worked long hours, Grampy looked after me for much of the time. It was he who pushed me for miles in my pram, took me to school and spent hours teaching me to read. When I was very small, I believed my name was 'Gal' as that was what he called me – a hangover from his time working at Portsmouth dockyard.

As he grew older, I dreaded the day when he would leave us. If he went to a Church meeting in the evening, I would lie awake, determined not to fall asleep until I heard him safely home. Shortly before he died, he gave me a white leather Bible which I carried on my wedding day. There is a rarely a day goes by when I do not think of Grampy.
Pamela Moore, Chandler's Ford

On this week

OCTOBER 10, 1975: **Richard Burton and Elizabeth Taylor secretly remarried in Johannesburg 16 months after getting divorced. Taylor said she decided to remarry after she feared spots found on her lungs were cancerous. Their stormy relationship didn't last and they separated again in 1976.**

In the garden

Autumn harvest

It's a great time to harvest the seeds from your best performing plants. Use a pair of clean and sharp garden scissors to cut the pods or seed heads from the plant and place them into a paper collection bag. Label all of your bags so that you do not forget which seeds are which before drying them out on a newspaper for a week.

I never knew that!

As much as 20 per cent of the world's oxygen is produced in the Amazon Rainforest. Its unique eco-system is home to at least 40,000 different plant species, nearly 430 species of mammals, 1,300 different kinds of birds and as many as 2.5 million different kinds of insects!

Wonderful wildlife on your doorstep!

PIC: ALAMY STOCK PHOTO

NAME: **Hedgehog**
HABITAT: **Grassland, hedgerows and woodland as well as urban gardens.**
DIET: **Insects including beetles, caterpillars and worms.**
LIFESPAN: **Up to seven years.**
FAST FACT: **Baby hoglets have soft spines that quickly harden after birth and as adults they'll have 5,000-7,000 spines.**

Recipe of the week

CHEESE AND DORSET ALE AND APPLE CHUTNEY PUFFS

SERVES: 10 PREP: 5 MINS COOK: 25 MINS

1 tbsp sunflower oil
1 carrot, peeled and diced small
1 parsnip, peeled and diced small
1 red onion, peeled and diced small
1 potato, peeled and diced small
2 tsp fresh thyme
75g (3oz) spinach, roughly chopped
8 tbsp Branston Dorset Ale and Apple Chutney
100g (4oz) reduced-fat mature cheddar cheese, cut into small cubes
2x 320g (11oz) sheets ready-rolled puff pastry
1 egg, beaten, for brushing
2 tbsp mixed seeds
Extra Branston Dorset Ale & Apple Chutney, to serve

1 Heat the oil in a saucepan and add the carrot, parsnip, onion and potato and fry for 3-4 mins. Reduce the heat, cover and cook for 5 mins, stirring. Add the spinach and thyme and cook for 2 mins until the spinach has cooked down. Remove from heat and cool.
2 Preheat oven to 190°C/375°F/Gas Mark 5. Line two baking trays with parchment. Cut the pastry into 10 equal pieces.
3 Mix the chutney and cheese into the filling. Place half of the pastry pieces on to the prepared trays and brush a 1cm border of beaten egg around each one.
4 Place the filling in the middle of each pastry piece. Put a second piece of pastry on top and press the edges together. Use a fork to seal the edges together firmly, giving a 1cm fluted border.
5 Slice a small air hole or two into the top of each pastry, and brush with the egg. Scatter with the seeds and bake for 20-25 mins until deep golden and the pastry is crisp. Serve hot, warm or cooled.
Branston Pickle

11 SUNDAY

12 MONDAY

13 TUESDAY

14 WEDNESDAY

15 THURSDAY

16 FRIDAY

17 SATURDAY

A magical memory

AN AMAZING ESCAPE

Here I am on my wedding day, wearing the beautiful lace dress made by my sister-in-law. I was amazingly lucky to be alive as I met my future husband just two weeks after I was discharged from hospital following a car crash in which two of the passengers were killed.

It happened when my friend Mary and I had gone dancing in the Tower ballroom at Blackpool. We had travelled there by coach, but were offered a lift home in a car with two young men we knew who lived near us.

I was in the front passenger seat tuning the radio when I looked up and saw we were heading towards a tree. I yelled at the driver but the next thing I knew I was lying in a field in the pitch dark. This was before the days of seatbelts and when I asked a policeman how I had escaped with no serious injuries he told me that instead of going through the windscreen I had gone through the roof when the car split in two. I should add that none of us had been drinking on the night of that tragic accident.

Eileen Coyne, Blackpool

On this week

OCTOBER 14, 1969: **A new coin fell into our purses as the seven-sided 50p replaced the ten-shilling note. As the only heptagonal coin in circulation worldwide, it prompted mixed responses including some who said it was 'ugly' and too easy to confuse with a half crown.**

In the garden

Bonkers for conkers

Autumn conkers have so many great uses from being made into decorations to bringing autumn into your home to keeping the spiders away. Conkers release a clever chemical that spiders seem to hate. Strategically placing them in corners and cool spots around the home should do the trick now that they're attempting to make their way in for the winter.

I never knew that!

Strawberries are not actually scientifically classed as berries and neither are raspberries or blackberries. Officially a berry has three layers, the skin, the fleshy part and the middle section where you find the seeds. Strangely, botanists do class bananas and cucumbers as berries!

Wonderful wildlife on your doorstep!

PIC: ALAMY STOCK PHOTO

NAME: **Wild Boar**
HABITAT: **Woodland areas, with main colonies located in Kent, East Sussex, Dorset, Devon and the Forest of Dean.**
DIET: **Plants, seeds, fruit, small mammals and birds.**
FAST FACT: **Hunted to extinction more than 400 years ago, wild boar were recently re-introduced into the UK during the Eighties.**

Recipe of the week

BLACKBERRY WAFFLES

SERVES: 4 PREP: 10 MINS COOK: 6 MINS

225g (8oz) mascarpone cheese
8 tbsp apricot jam
200g (7oz) blackberries
8 waffles

1 Toast 4 of the waffles.
2 Arrange 4 waffles on work surface. Spread 2 tbsp mascarpone and 2 tbsp apricot jam on each.
3 Arrange a few blackberries on each in a single layer. Top each with 1 of remaining waffles and press down firmly.
4 Set the grill to low and cook for about 3 mins or until warmed through. Serve immediately.
www.driscolls.com

18 SUNDAY

19 MONDAY

20 TUESDAY

21 WEDNESDAY

22 THURSDAY

23 FRIDAY

24 SATURDAY

A magical memory

FRIENDS FOR LIFE

My friend Doreen (on the right in the photo) and I met in 1942 when she had been bombed out of her home in Islington and came to live three doors away from me in Harrow. I was aged four, she was three and we have been friends ever since.

Our shared memories include the street party we had to celebrate the end of the war in 1945, both of us performing in plays put on by the youth club, and both going to secretarial college. In 1958 we both became engaged to our boyfriends and got married the following year. In 1962, we were both pregnant and gave birth to daughters. More recently, we have both survived cancer.

Although Doreen and her husband moved away to Devon, we always keep in touch and see each other when possible. I am now a widow, but I'm glad to say that Doreen and Alan are still going strong.

We have shared all our fears and happy moments over the years. I am so grateful that I have had this lifelong friendship.
Iris Platten, Bushey Heath

On this week

OCTOBER 21, 1996: **Oscar-winning plasticine models Wallace and Gromit were reunited with their creator, Nick Park, after being left accidentally in the boot of a New York taxi. The missing models had sparked an appeal to all police stations in the city.**

In the garden

Autumn colours

There's nothing quite like the beautiful colours of autumn. If you think your garden might be lacking autumnal tones go for plants like beauty berry, virginia creeper and chrysanthemums. Cornus in particular are great as once their leaves fall off, the beautiful bright branches are revealed.

I never knew that!

The main ship scenes (not including those set in the present day) of the film Titanic (1997) are approximately 2 hours and 40 minutes long, which is how long the real Titanic took to sink. Also, while the character of Jack Dawson is fictional, records do show a J. Dawson was aboard the real Titanic.

Wonderful wildlife on your doorstep!

PIC: ALAMY STOCK PHOTO

NAME. **Red squirrel**
HABITAT: **Woodland, although classed as near-threatened in England, Wales and Northern Ireland.**
DIET: **Seeds, buds, flowers, berries, nuts, fruit, fungi and insects.**
FAST FACT: **Baby squirrels are called kittens and are born without hair and teeth and with their eyes closed.**

Recipe of the week

LEEK AND CHEESE MUFFINS

MAKES: 10 PREP: 10 MINS COOK: 20 MINS
225g (8oz) self-raising flour
1 leek, finely sliced
Freshly ground black pepper
100g (4oz) half-fat cheddar, grated
175ml (¼ pt) semi-skimmed milk
1 egg
50ml (2 fl oz) olive oil
10 cherry tomatoes

1 Preheat the oven to 200°C/400°F/Gas Mark 6.
2 In a mixing bowl, combine the flour, leek, freshly ground black pepper and cheddar and mix well.
3 In a separate bowl, mix together the milk, egg and olive oil. Add this mixture to the dry ingredients and mix well.
4 Grease ten muffin moulds and half-fill each with the mix.
5 Prick each cherry tomato – this stops them popping when they cook – and press one tomato into the top of each spoonful of mix.
6 Spoon the remaining mixture over each muffin to conceal the tomato. Cook for about 20 mins until golden brown.
www.british-leeks.co.uk

25 SUNDAY

26 MONDAY

27 TUESDAY

28 WEDNESDAY

29 THURSDAY

30 FRIDAY

31 SATURDAY

A magical memory

A TRUE GIRL GUIDE

Here I am on my wedding day, joyfully surrounded by Brownies and Guides. I have happy memories of being a Brownie, then a Guide and, later, a Land Ranger.

I wasn't very confident as a youngster but Brownies opened my eyes to the world and set me up for life.

As a Guide, I flourished - gaining Interest Badges, going to my first camp, visiting Holland. In the Rangers we planned days out and weekends away and felt very grown up. At seventeen I became a Tawny Owl and took over the Pack. Three years later I was encouraged to continue as a Guide Captain which involved taking the girls away for Youth Hostelling weekends. Pretty scary at that age!

As an adult I have had many roles including Division Commissioner for Uxbridge and being a trainer. It was really good to welcome inexperienced Guiders to one of my courses and watch them grow. When we moved to Hampshire I became a member of two Trefoil Guilds. The skills I have learned over the years have made me a true Girl Guide - long may it continue!

June Jones, Ringwood

On this week

OCTOBER 25, 1979: **We bid goodbye to Basil, Sybil, Manuel and Polly as the hotel doors closed for a final time on Fawlty Towers. The sitcom gave us four years of belly laughs from 'don't mention the war' to the 'waldorf salad' joke.**

In the garden

Hallowe'en pumpkin

It's Hallowe'en season and many of you will have a pumpkin on your doorstep that your grandchildren have helped you carve out. To keep it looking fresh and healthy throughout the week, dip a cloth in bleach and wipe all over the outside to preserve it, focusing on the carved areas.

I never knew that!

England's Met Office and Ireland's Met Eireann name storms that affect the UK if they reach an amber 'be prepared' status. They're named alphabetically and alternate between male and female names, although there are no storms beginning with the letters Q, U, X, Y and Z. Last year we met Storm Freya and Storm Gareth.

Wonderful wildlife on your doorstep!

PIC: ALAMY STOCK PHOTO

NAME: **Hazel dormouse**
HABITAT: **Woodland, hedgerows and scrub land.**
DIET: **Pollen, fruit, nuts and insects.**
FAST FACT: **Dormice are a sleepy bunch that hibernate for around six months over winter. They're classed as rare and vulnerable to extinction in the UK.**

Recipe of the week

CARROT & GOAT'S CHEESE TARTS

SERVES: 4 PREP: 20 MINS COOK: 30 MINS

250g (9oz) Chantenay carrots
1 x 320-350g sheet ready-rolled all-butter puff pastry
85g (3oz) goat's cheese
Half a jar tomato pesto
1 tbsp olive oil
Sea salt flakes and freshly ground black pepper
A small handful chopped fresh chives

1 Preheat oven to 220°C/425°F/Gas Mark 7 and line a baking sheet with non-stick baking paper.
2 Cut the Chantenay carrots into quarters and lightly steam until just tender.
3 Unroll the pastry onto the baking paper and cut into whatever shapes you like. Prick the base with a fork.
4 Bake in the oven for 12-15 mins until puffed up and golden brown.
5 Remove the tart bases from the oven and smear with tomato pesto. Top with carrots and sliced goat's cheese. Drizzle with olive oil and sprinkle with salt and pepper.
6 Return the tarts to the oven and bake for 5-7 mins until the cheese has just melted. Remove from the oven, scatter over the chives and serve.
chantenay.co.uk

1 SUNDAY

2 MONDAY

3 TUESDAY

4 WEDNESDAY

5 THURSDAY

6 FRIDAY

7 SATURDAY

A magical memory

IN SICKNESS AND IN HEALTH

This is my father on his motorbike when he was in his early 20s. Underneath his biking gear he was wearing thermals and thick pyjamas with a pullover on top to keep warm on the long journey he made regularly to visit my mother (then his fiancée) in hospital.

Mum had tried to cool things off between them as she was suffering from tuberculosis and wasn't expected to live. Dad wouldn't hear of it and they married in 1947 after he finished his stint in the Air Force.

Mum eventually underwent a pneumonectomy (removal of the lung). Although the operation was successful, her general health deteriorated. Against doctor's orders, Dad smuggled her back home where, with better food and hygiene, she made a full recovery.

Mum had been advised not to have children as it might endanger her life but she was not easily put off and I was born after they had been married for ten years. Mum lived until she was 80 - no mean feat, given her medical history. She and Dad had a lasting, happy union that had begun in teenage years. **Linda Kettle, Portsmouth**

On this week

NOVEMBER 2, 1982: **Channel 4 went on air for the first time. Countdown, hosted by Richard Whiteley and a lexicographer called Mary was the first programme to air on the new station, followed later in the day by the first episode of Brookside.**

In the garden

Bat box

Putting up a bat box to house our nocternal friends is a great way to help take care of them. There are a few ways you can attract bats to your garden - these include creating a pond, planting a hedge and attracting moths with an outside lamp - the bats will be drawn to the moths especially in the evening.

I never knew that!

William Shakespeare influences us more day-to-day than you might think. Phrases including 'fair play', 'in a pickle' and 'dead as a doornail' were all coined by the renowned playwright. He used Latin sparingly in his work, which is unusual for the time, but he did include the word Honorificabilitudinitatibus in Love's Labour's Lost - now that's not one we'll be repeating!

Wonderful wildlife on your doorstep!

PIC: ALAMY STOCK PHOTO

NAME:
Little Owl
HABITAT:
Farmland, parkland and open woodland.
DIET: **Small mammals, birds as well as beetles, crickets and worms.**
FAST FACT:
Little owls are not native to the UK and weren't introduced until the 19th Century. Unlike other owls, little owls can often be seen in daylight.

Recipe of the week

PICKLE, PINK PEPPERCORN AND HONEY-GLAZED HAM

SERVES: 10 PREP: 10 MINS COOK: 2 HOURS PLUS RESTING

1.2kg (2lb 5oz) unsmoked boneless gammon joint
6 bay leaves
1½ tbsp pink peppercorns, lightly crushed
4 tbsp Branston Smooth Pickle
3 tbsp runny honey

1 Place the gammon in a large pan. Add enough water to completely cover the meat, along with bay leaves, and bring to the boil. Once boiling, reduce the heat and cook at a gentle simmer for 2 hours. (If using a larger or smaller joint, allow 20 mins per 450g, plus an extra 20 mins), drain and leave until cool enough to handle.
2 Heat oven to 180°C/350°F/Gas Mark 4. Using a sharp knife, carefully slice away the skin (rind) from the meat, leaving a 5mm-1cm layer of fat on the meat. Discard the skin, score the fat well and transfer the joint to a large lined baking tin.
3 Mix together the peppercorns, pickle and honey, and liberally brush the mixture over the meat. Bake for 20-30 mins until the glaze is sticky and thick but not burnt.
4 Serve hot, or cold with green beans, carrots and new potatoes.
Branston Pickle

8 SUNDAY

9 MONDAY

10 TUESDAY

11 WEDNESDAY

12 THURSDAY

13 FRIDAY

14 SATURDAY

A magical memory

YEAH YEAH YEAH!

It was 1963, I was thirteen, and the The Beatles were coming to my home town of York. To say I was excited was an understatement.

My father was a policeman and as pop stars didn't have their own security in those days, it was up to the police to keep everyone safe. As a thank you they were given concessionary tickets and my dad had one. What a thrill!

On the evening, the tension of waiting for the group to arrive and the girls screaming was almost unbearable. When they did appear, we were told that John Lennon had a sore throat and he was unusually quiet. Up until then Paul McCartney had been my favourite but I changed my mind as George Harrison showed how talented he was and sung his heart out. Others must have thought the same as they were throwing jelly babies on stage because he had once said he liked them.

I imagined they would be staying at a posh hotel but discovered The Beatles were actually booked into a small motel on the Tadcaster Road close to where I lived. So near and yet so far!

Christine Regan, Nottingham

On this week

NOVEMBER 9, 1985: **It was a fairytale moment, seeing Princess Diana dancing with John Travolta at a gala dinner hosted by President Reagan and his wife Nancy. The gala took place on the first day of Diana and Charles' first royal trip together to the USA.**

In the garden

Sharpening your tools

Use a fine metal file to sharpen the blunt edges of your garden sheers, forks, knives, secateurs and hoes. Pop some lubricating oil on the tool and file with forward motion and downward pressure. You'll also want to remove any rust with a wire brush before wiping with an oily rag.

I never knew that!

It takes 10 litres of milk to make one kilogram of the UK's favourite cheese – Cheddar. There are around 700 named cheeses made here in the UK. The nation's second favourite cheese is apparently Mozzarella and surprisingly the variety we most buy is also made here in the UK.

Wonderful wildlife on your doorstep!

PIC: ALAMY STOCK PHOTO

NAME: **Golden eagle**
HABITAT: **Wild open moorlands of Scotland.**
DIET: **Grouse, rabbits, hares, deer and even young farm livestock.**
FAST FACT. **This unlikely bird is actually often named as the national bird of Scotland. They have an impressive wingspan of 2.2 metres.**

Recipe of the week

SAUSAGE AND CARAMELISED ONION HOT POT

SERVES: 4-6 PREP: 10 MINS COOK: 30 MINS

2 tbsp vegetable oil
6 sausages
300g (10½ oz) carrots, sliced
2 tbsp cornflour
2 tbsp Branston Caramelised Onion Chutney
700ml (1 ¼ pt) vegetable stock
600g (1lb 3oz) leftover cooked broccoli, sprouts and peas or any vegetables you have leftover
700g (1lb 8oz) leftover cooked potatoes, chopped
400g (14oz) butter beans
1 tbsp Worcestershire sauce
Ground black pepper
Fresh flat-leaf parsley, for garnish

1 Heat the oil in a large saucepan and fry the sausages until browned. Add the carrots and cook, stirring, for a further 2 mins.
2 Stir in the cornflour and then the Branston Caramelised Onion Chutney, cooking for 1 min. Gradually add the stock, stirring as you go. Remove the sausages and roughly chop, before returning them to the saucepan.
3 Bring to the boil, then add the leftover vegetables, potatoes and butter beans, and mix in the Worcestershire sauce and season with pepper. Simmer, covered, for 30 mins.
4 Serve, garnished with parsley.
Branston Pickle

15 SUNDAY

16 MONDAY

17 TUESDAY

18 WEDNESDAY

19 THURSDAY

20 FRIDAY

21 SATURDAY

A magical memory

A TREASURED PRIZE

One of my most treasured books was given to me by my grandma when I was aged eleven. I often stayed with my maternal grandparents during the school holidays. They lived in a village in Essex with a huge garden, lots of cats, an old wind-up gramophone and many books. What heaven!

I was an avid reader then and still am now. My grandma had been given the book, The Wide, Wide World by Elizabeth Wetherell, as a school prize for 'punctuality and regular attendance'. The book is now 134 years old and in a worn condition, but that adds to its charm. The print is so small that I can't read it, even with my glasses on. After some research I found that the book is still available and I was able to download it on to my Kindle to read it in a large font.

My beautiful granddaughter is now nearly eleven and she often comes to stay with us. Next time she comes I am going to give her the book. My dear grandma would be pleased to know her prized book will be owned by her great great granddaughter.
Jenny Tyler, Leigh-on-Sea

On this week

NOVEMBER 19, 1994: **And the winning numbers are... Britain excitedly clutched their tickets for the first-ever lottery draw, hosted by Noel Edmonds. 15 million players bought some 35 million tickets in the hope of winning the £5.9m jackpot that was eventually split between seven winners.**

In the garden
Helping hedgehogs
Leave an area of your garden wild for grass to grow and leaves to pile up. This will not only attract hedgehogs to the bugs living in this area but it will give them a nesting place. Make sure they have plenty of fresh water about as well as canned and dry dog and cat food.

I never knew that!
Egyptians were one of the earliest users of make-up, concocting products for the eyes, cheeks and lips using ground nuts, minerals, animal fat and vegetable oil. It wasn't just the women who would paint their faces, men would too.

Wonderful wildlife on your doorstep!

PIC: ALAMY STOCK PHOTO

NAME: **Wood mouse**
HABITAT: **Various including urban gardens, woodland and moorland.**
DIET: **Seeds, plants, animal foods and insects.**
FAST FACT: **This common mouse will gather a food store in autumn which they store in their underground burrow or even in old birds' nests.**

Recipe of the week

KALE, SPELT & CHORIZO SOUP

SERVES: 4 PREP: 10 MINS COOK: 20 MINS

2 tbsp rapeseed or sunflower oil
1 onion, chopped
2 cooking chorizo sausages, skins removed, crumbled into small pieces
1 dried red chilli or a good pinch of chilli flakes, to taste
4 tomatoes, finely chopped, or 1 tbsp organic tomato purée
150g (5oz) pearled spelt, rinsed well and drained
1.5 litres (2½ pt) chicken or good vegetable stock
Salt and black pepper
200g (7oz) curly kale, leaves stripped from their stalks and roughly chopped

1 Heat the oil in a pan over a low heat, add the onion and fry gently for 10 mins, stirring now and then to stop it catching, until soft and translucent. Add the chorizo and fry, stirring occasionally, for a few minutes more.
2 Stir in the chilli, tomatoes, spelt and stock and season with salt and pepper. Bring to the boil, reduce the heat and simmer for 20 mins.
3 Meanwhile, blanch and squeeze the kale. Add to the pan and cook for a further 15 mins or until the spelt is tender.
4 Keep an eye on the liquid and top up a little if needed. Check seasoning.
www.soilassociation.org

22 SUNDAY

23 MONDAY

24 TUESDAY

25 WEDNESDAY

26 THURSDAY

27 FRIDAY

28 SATURDAY

A magical memory

GLORIOUS FOOD

Growing up in the Fifties, there was one food I disliked immensely - junket! I hated its slimy consistency but food was rationed and we were encouraged to eat what we were given. My dear mother liked tripe (cow's intestines cooked with onion). It had an evil smell and was particularly unappetising to look at.

Boiled beef pudding was a popular dish. My mother lined a greased pudding dish with pastry before adding beef and leek with a little gravy mix. The pudding was placed in saucepan to steam for several hours before being served with potatoes and greens from the garden. Delicious! On Mondays, any veg remaining from the Sunday roast was mashed, lightly floured and fried in lard to make bubble and squeak.

Dessert was nearly always a milk pudding of some description - rice, sago, semolina or tapioca (often described as frog's spawn!). Blancmange was made from a packet of powder mixed with milk and sugar, brought to the boil, then left to set in a glass mould.

For breakfast we had porridge, my father's speciality. It involved lots of stirring and he always added a little salt.
Sheila Mills, Minehead

On this week

NOVEMBER 22, 1946: **The Biro pen, an invention by the Hungarian journalist, Ladislao Biro, first went on sale. It used a tiny ball bearing in its tip so the ball rotated to pick up ink from the cartridge and leave it on the paper.**

In the garden

Fat balls for birds

All you need to make these tasty balls for birds is vegetable or beef suet or lard, plus bird seed mix. Mix one-part suet to two-parts seed before transferring to a saucepan and gently heating, stirring until the fat melts. Mould the mix into balls with your hands before tying on to tree branches with string.

I never knew that!

Marie Antoinette was forbidden from riding horses because it was deemed too dangerous. Desperate to be able to ride a compromise was reached and she and her ladies rode donkeys instead! The French Queen and all her ladies would take regular donkey trips to the forest on their noble steeds.

Wonderful wildlife on your doorstep!

PIC: ALAMY STOCK PHOTO

NAME: **Grey heron**
HABITAT: **Rivers, lakes, garden ponds and canals across the UK.**
DIET: **Fish, small mammals, amphibians and small birds.**
FAST FACT: **Despite their large size, herons nest in the tops of trees using nests created out of twigs usually alongside other herons' nests in colonies.**

Recipe of the week

PORK WITH ENGLISH PESTO CRUST

SERVES: 2 PREP: 10 MINS COOK: 25-30 MINS

100g (4oz) walnut pieces
1 tbsp English mustard
1 clove garlic
1 pot flat-leaf parsley
75g (3oz) cheddar cheese, grated
1 tbsp oil
4 pork loin steaks, trimmed
200g (7oz) vine on cherry tomatoes

1 Preheat the oven to 200°C/400°F/Gas Mark 6.
2 Place the walnuts, mustard, garlic and all except 3 sprigs of the parsley, including stalks, into a food processor and blitz to produce a pesto paste. Add in the cheddar and process to combine and season.
3 Heat the oil in a frying pan and fry the pork steaks to brown on both sides for about 5 mins then transfer to a baking tray.
4 Press the pesto over the steaks, add the tomatoes, still on the vine, to the tray and roast for 15-20 mins.
5 Serve the pork topped with the tomatoes, sprinkled with remaining chopped parsley and new potatoes.
www.lovefreshherbs.co.uk

29 SUNDAY

30 MONDAY

1 TUESDAY

2 WEDNESDAY

3 THURSDAY

4 FRIDAY

5 SATURDAY

A magical memory

MY CHILDHOOD HOME

I was a baby when we moved to Grove Cottage on the Drakelowe estate in Derbyshire. My father worked at Grove Farm. We were a large family and our kitchen was always a hive of activity. Our mother was never very happy on Mondays which was wash day.

It was quite a skill to put a large wet sheet through the mangle, feeding it through with one hand while turning the handle with the other. I loved Tuesdays when she did the ironing using flat irons heated by the fire. There was always a slightly scorched smell and a whiff of Robin starch.

In between cooking, washing, ironing and scrubbing, my mother would sew. She made curtains, cushions, dresses and coats and did alterations for other people. Her hands were never free, when she wasn't at her sewing machine, she was sitting by the fire in the front room, knitting or crocheting.

We had a large garden full of lovely cottage-garden flowers my mother grew and delighted in giving away to local people. Dad grew enough vegetables to keep us almost self-sufficient. I could write much more - it seems like only yesterday I left Grove Cottage.
Gwen Cooper, Walton-on-Trent

On this week

DECEMBER 3, 1988: **We'd all been told to go to work on an egg and then health minister Edwina Currie announced most British eggs were infected with salmonella. The claims were later found to be unsubstantiated but the comment provoked a public scandal.**

In the garden

Make a wreath

Raid your garden for anything that might look festive as part of a Christmas wreath. Items such as conifer leaves, sprigs of holly, ivy and pine cones work well. Once you've got all your materials, you'll need to cut them to size before using wire to arrange them into a traditional wreath shape.

I never knew that!

When Coronation Street first aired in December 1960 it was filmed live and it wasn't until the following March that episodes began to be pre-recorded - taking some pressure off the cast and crew! Ken Barlow, played by William Roache, is the only character who has been on the street since that very first episode.

Wonderful wildlife on your doorstep!

PIC: ALAMY STOCK PHOTO

NAME: **New Forest pony**
HABITAT: **The grassland and open woodland of the New Forest National Park.**
DIET: **Grass and select green plants.**
FAST FACT: **Although they freely roam the New Forest, the ponies are all owned by 'commoners' who have the right to graze their animals in the forest.**

Recipe of the week

APRICOT AND CHESTNUT STUFFING BALLS

MAKES: 18 PREP: 10 MINS COOK: 35 MINS

A little butter, to grease
1 large brown onion, coarsely chopped
225g (8oz) dried apricots, finely chopped
225g (8oz) dried white breadcrumbs
75g (3oz) butter
225g (8oz) frozen chestnuts, thawed & coarsely chopped
Bunch fresh parsley, chopped
Salt and pepper

1 Preheat the oven to 200°C/400°F/Gas Mark 6.
2 Grease a roasting tray with butter.
3 Place the onion and apricot in a saucepan, pour in a little hot water and boil for 5 mins. Drain, tip into a large mixing bowl and stir in the breadcrumbs.
4 Melt the 75g (3oz) of butter in a frying pan and pour half into the mixing bowl with the breadcrumbs. Add the chestnuts to the frying pan and cook over a high heat for a couple of minutes until lightly browned. Tip the chestnuts into the breadcrumb mixture, add the parsley, season and mix well.
5 Using your hands, shape into approx 18 balls. Place in the roasting dish and bake for 30 mins, uncovered, until crisp and piping hot.
Lakeland

6 SUNDAY

7 MONDAY

8 TUESDAY

9 WEDNESDAY

10 THURSDAY

11 FRIDAY

12 SATURDAY

A magical memory

CHRISTMAS PAST AND PRESENT

The little girl on the left in this picture might well be me - it was taken in Blackburn in the Fifties. Christmas was a poor affair when I was growing up in those soot-laden streets. My earliest memory is when my brother and I nearly got arrested for stealing a branch off the big Christmas tree in the Square. When I saw the branch lying on the ground, I picked it up, intending to take it home as we could not afford a tree of our own. Two policemen let us go with a stern warning not to steal again!

On Christmas morning I walked to the Blackburn Ragged School clutching the precious ticket I had endured many Sunday sermons for. I queued with other excited children for a breakfast of pork pie, orange juice and a piece of fruit. After that we queued again at long tables weighed down with donated toys. Sadly, my dream present - a doll's house - was given to the girl in front of me and I received a doll with one arm missing.

This year I will be in New York where I will discover the magic of Christmas with my daughter.
Christine McCherry, Blackpool

On this week

DECEMBER 9, 1960: **The first-ever episode of the much-loved soap Coronation Street was shown on TV in black and white. It introduced what would become hugely popular characters on the cobbles including Elsie Tanner, Ken Barlow, Ena Sharples and Annie Walker.**

In the garden

Give the gift of gardening

Giving planted presents to your loved ones at Christmas is a great gift idea that will last. Why not give them a small potted plant of some herbs they might like by wrapping the plant pot up in some hessian fabric and a nice festive bow? They'll be able to keep going back to those herbs year-round, remembering what a lovely thoughtful gift you got them.

I never knew that!

A staggering 24.4 million viewers tuned in on Christmas Day 2003 to watch the last-ever episode of Only Fools and Horses. The final farewell entitled Sleepless in Peckham saw the Trotter family at last find their fortune, when dear old uncle Albert leaves Del and Rodney money in his Will.

Wonderful wildlife on your doorstep!

PIC: ALAMY STOCK PHOTO

NAME: **Stoat**

HABITAT: **Widespread across the UK in woodland, heathland, farmland, grassland and coastal areas.**

DIET: **Small mammals including water voles and rabbits – even though they're often smaller than their prey.**

FAST FACT: **Stoats, although similar to the weasel, are bigger and can be recognised by their black-tipped tail. Baby stoats are called kits.**

Recipe of the week

GAMMON AND ROAST POTATO HASH BROWNS

SERVES: 2 PREP: 10 MINS COOK: 20 MINS

300g (10½ oz) cooked roast potatoes
150g (5oz) cooked gammon
2 tbsp flour
3 medium eggs
1½ tbsp goose fat (or vegetable oil)

1 Cut the potatoes and gammon into small pieces (just under 1cm) and add to a bowl. Season, toss with the flour and mix in 1 beaten egg. Scrunch everything together and press firmly into 4 patties (8cm across, 2cm deep). Chill them for at least 15 mins, or for up to 12 hours.

2 Heat the goose fat (or oil) in a heavy-based, non-stick frying pan. Add the hash brown patties and cook on the lowest heat for 10 mins, until a crust has formed. Flip over and repeat on the other side, until golden and piping hot in the centre. Remove from the pan and keep warm.

3 Return the pan to a high heat. Add the remaining eggs to the fat in the pan. Fry for 1-2 mins, spooning the excess fat over the yolks, until cooked to your liking.

4 Season and serve on top of the hash browns. Delicious with wilted spinach and ketchup or brown sauce.

www.waitrose.com/recipes

13 SUNDAY

14 MONDAY

15 TUESDAY

16 WEDNESDAY

17 THURSDAY

18 FRIDAY

19 SATURDAY

A magical memory

A CHRISTMAS CAROL

This is me with my favourite doll. She was a Christmas present so I called her Carol, as in 'Christmas carol'. She looked like a real baby and I loved to push her around in my pram. She came with a wooden crib which I later discovered had been made by my dad, not by Santa's little helpers. I loved to dress her in proper baby clothes – cardigans, bootees, bonnets and mittens knitted by my mum and Nanny Alice – although they were really too big for her.

I was very fortunate as I always received a doll for Christmas but my first one, Carol, was my favourite. The Mary Make-up doll and Action Girl (a female version of Action Man) couldn't compare. Sadly, I lost Carol somewhere along the way when our family moved from Birmingham to Bolton when I was fourteen. At that age I had different priorities such as dreaming about having a boyfriend, reading Jackie magazine and pinning posters on my bedroom wall.

Jane Hodkinson, via email

On this week

DECEMBER 31, 1973: **The Conservative government, led by Edward Heath, announced the start of the three-day working week because of limited fuel supplies brought on by industrial disputes. TV companies were also obliged to stop broadcasting past 10.30pm to conserve electricity.**

In the garden

Taking care of mistletoe

The romantic plant can become very dry inside so it's important to not bring your sprig of mistletoe inside until the time is right. To keep it looking fresh indoors, you can try spraying it with cold water regularly to make it appear less dry. When handling it, take care not to touch the berries, ensuring you wash your hands after touching because of their poisonous properties.

I never knew that!

It's one of the world's best-loved festive films and according to Maureen O'Hara, the original Miracle on 34th Street nearly had a sequel. She claimed that co-star John Payne wanted to do another and had even written the screenplay. Sadly, he died before getting to share his work.

Wonderful wildlife on your doorstep!

PIC: ALAMY STOCK PHOTO

NAME:
Red Deer
HABITAT:
Woodland and moorland through the UK, although most of the red deer population is found in Scotland.
DIET: **Grass, shrubs, tree shoots and bark.**
FAST FACT:
The second of Britain's native deer, those that live in woodland often grow larger than those living in open areas, because the food quality is better.

Recipe of the week

SPICY SPROUT, FENNEL AND PEPPER STIR-FRY

SERVES: 4 PREP: 15 MINS COOK: 20 MINS

500g (1lb 2oz) Brussels sprouts
45g (1½ oz) coconut chunks
1 tbsp vegetable oil
1 large fennel bulb, very thinly sliced
2 red peppers, deseeded and thinly sliced
4 cloves garlic, thinly sliced
1½ tsp cumin seeds
400ml (14 fl oz) can coconut milk
1 tsp vegetable bouillon powder
¼ tsp dried chilli flakes

1 Trim and halve the Brussels sprouts. Place in a saucepan, cover with boiling water and cook for 3 mins. Drain well. Grate the pieces of coconut, chopping the pieces that become a little too small to grate. Keep the chopped coconut separate.
2 Heat the oil in a pan and fry the fennel and peppers for 5 mins, stirring frequently. Add the sprouts and fry for 3 mins. Stir in the chopped coconut, garlic and cumin and fry for a further 2 mins. Stir in the coconut milk, bouillon powder and chilli flakes and simmer gently for a further 3-5 mins until hot and bubbling.
3 Spoon into bowls and scatter with the grated coconut.
www.waitrose.com/recipes

20 SUNDAY

21 MONDAY

22 TUESDAY

23 WEDNESDAY

24 THURSDAY

25 FRIDAY

26 SATURDAY

A magical memory

THE FAB FOUR IN PANTO

It was Boxing Day 1963, I was just eight years old, and my older sister and her boyfriend were going to see The Beatles in a Christmas show at the Hammersmith Odeon. My other sister, aged thirteen was the biggest Beatles fan ever (along with thousands of other girls her age!), and was miffed that she could not go.

Then, about two hours before my father was due to drop them off for the concert, our mother told us to go and get ready as we were going to see them too. Talk about the best Christmas present ever! You can imagine the excitement as we got dressed.

The traffic was at a standstill so we walked the last part of the way. We were in the stalls, my sister and her boyfriend had better seats in the dress circle. The Beatles played a little panto scene dressed as old women before the audience realised it was them and the place erupted. The screaming was deafening - talk about Beatlemania! I have never forgotten that night and am so glad I saw them. (In our family photo, I'm second on the left, next to Mum.)
Jennifer Phillips, via email

On this week

DECEMBER 25, 1952: **It was all ears for Her Majesty as Queen Elizabeth made the first Christmas broadcast of her reign. She sat at the same desk and chair her father King George VI and his father had done to make the festive royal speech.**

In the garden

Prevent freezing pipes

To avoid your outside pipes freezing up over winter, try turning off the water supply to the outside and insulate the taps with pipe insulating sleeves along the full length of the pipe, taping it up to secure it. It's very important to invest in some good pipe insulation to save energy and reduce the heat flow from outside.

I never knew that!

Since 1952, the Queen has delivered a message every year except in 1969, when her greeting was a written address. The very first Christmas address was written by Rudyard Kipling in 1932 and was delivered by her grandfather King George V. The first televised message was broadcast by the Queen in 1957.

Wonderful wildlife on your doorstep!

PIC: ALAMY STOCK PHOTO

NAME: **Robin**
HABITAT: **Woodland, urban and suburban gardens. Most stay in the UK all year round.**
DIET: **Worms, seeds, fruit and insects.**
FAST FACT: **Both female and male robins have red breasts. Juveniles moult their brown baby feathers at around three months old.**

Recipe of the week

BUTTERED SPROUTS WITH BACON AND WALNUTS

SERVES: 4 PREP: 5 MINS COOK: 6 MINS

600g (1lb 3oz) Brussels sprouts
4 rashers of streaky bacon, chopped
25g (1oz) walnuts, coarsely chopped
25g (1oz) butter

1 Place the sprouts in a pan of salted, boiling water cook for 5 mins then drain.
2 Heat a large frying pan fry the bacon until crisp then add the walnuts and fry for 1 min.
3 Add the sprouts and the butter and cook, stirring often, until lightly browned.
Lakeland

27 SUNDAY

28 MONDAY

29 TUESDAY

30 WEDNESDAY

31 THURSDAY

1 FRIDAY

2 SATURDAY

A magical memory

A CHEEKY LITTLE WINE

My parents drank wine on Sundays, Christmas and special occasions. It was always homemade. Mother's attempts at making wine started with my grandfather, her father-in-law. She took to it with great enthusiasm. Every year after my father's harvest of parsnips from the garden or using blackberries gleaned from the lanes, my mother would install her vats of fermenting wine on the floor of our large airing cupboard.

The vats were covered with thick brown blankets. Sometimes when I pulled out clean clothes they fell on top of the blankets. Disaster would strike when knickers and socks descended with a momentum that took them into the wine, blanket and all. I would simply wring out the offending items and put them somewhere to dry.

Hearing the grown-ups later discussing the merits of a glass of wine never made me feel guilty. In my ignorance, I assumed that wine with 'a hint of old sock' or 'musty blanket' was no different to any other as in my childish opinion all wine had a nasty taste.

The photo is of me (on the left) with my sisters in the garden of our house.
Nicolette Gunn, Gillingham

On this week

DECEMBER 30, 1942: **We first discovered Ol' Blue Eyes himself as Frank Sinatra made his solo singing performance at New York's Paramount Theatre. Outside the theatre fans called 'bobby soxers' because of their classic poodle skirt with white socks caused a riot because they were so excited.**

In the garden

Leftovers for birds

It's really important to know what and what not to give to birds from the Christmas leftovers. Meats are a no-no as they go off fairly quickly. Snacks such as nuts and pretzels are also bad as they contain a lot of salt. Sweeter treats are better for them, such as crumbs from the Christmas cake, mince pies and biscuits. Dried porridge oats, fruit and mild grated cheese are also good for birds.

I never knew that!

Everyone wants to start the New Year afresh, but some New Year's superstitions across the world are rather unusual. Estonians eat up to 12 meals to give them strength, in Ecuador scarecrow effigies are burnt at midnight to cleanse away negative energy, while in Spain eating 12 grapes while the bells chime promises good fortune!

Wonderful wildlife on your doorstep!

PIC: ALAMY STOCK PHOTO

NAME: **Scottish wildcat**
HABITAT: **Woodland bordering open areas in the Scottish Highlands.**
DIET: **Rabbits, small mammals and small birds.**
FAST FACT: **The Scottish wildcat is the rarest mammal in Great Britain, with research suggesting there are under 400 left in the wild.**

Recipe of the week

LEFTOVER TURKEY CURRY

SERVES: 4 PREP: 15 MINS COOK: 20 MINS

1 large onion, finely chopped
30ml (1fl oz) olive oil
1 green chilli, finely chopped, no seeds
2 tbsp curry powder
400g (14oz) chunky chopped tomatoes
400ml (14fl oz) coconut milk
100ml (4fl oz) boiling water
20ml (½ fl oz) lemon juice
1 tbsp mango chutney
1 chicken stock cube
450g (1lb) cooked leftover turkey meat
5g (¼ oz) fresh coriander, chopped

1 In a pan sauté the onion in the olive oil until softened.
2 Add the chilli and the curry powder to the pan and cook gently for a few minutes.
3 Add the tomatoes, coconut milk, boiling water, lemon juice and mango chutney and crumble in the stock cube.
4 Stir well and gently simmer for 20 mins.
5 Add the turkey and heat through, gently.
6 Sprinkle with coriander and serve with rice and naan bread.
Aldi.co.uk

2020 year-to-view calendar

JANUARY

M		6	13	20	27
Tu		7	14	21	28
W	1	8	15	22	29
Th	2	9	16	23	30
F	3	10	17	24	31
Sa	4	11	18	25	
Su	5	12	19	26	

FEBRUARY

M		3	10	17	24
Tu		4	11	18	25
W		5	12	19	26
Th		6	13	20	27
F		7	14	21	28
Sa	1	8	15	22	29
Su	2	9	16	23	

MARCH

M		2	9	16	23	30
Tu		3	10	17	24	31
W		4	11	18	25	
Th		5	12	19	26	
F		6	13	20	27	
Sa		7	14	21	28	
Su	1	8	15	22	29	

APRIL

M		6	13	20	27
Tu		7	14	21	28
W	1	8	15	22	29
Th	2	9	16	23	30
F	3	10	17	24	
Sa	4	11	18	25	
Su	5	12	19	26	

MAY

M		4	11	18	25
Tu		5	12	19	26
W		6	13	20	27
Th		7	14	21	28
F	1	8	15	22	29
Sa	2	9	16	23	30
Su	3	10	17	24	31

JUNE

M	1	8	15	22	29
Tu	2	9	16	23	30
W	3	10	17	24	
Th	4	11	18	25	
F	5	12	19	26	
Sa	6	13	20	27	
Su	7	14	21	28	

JULY

M		6	13	20	27
Tu		7	14	21	28
W	1	8	15	22	29
Th	2	9	16	23	30
F	3	10	17	24	31
Sa	4	11	18	25	
Su	5	12	19	26	

AUGUST

M		3	10	17	24	31
Tu		4	11	18	25	
W		5	12	19	26	
Th		6	13	20	27	
F		7	14	21	28	
Sa	1	8	15	22	29	
Su	2	9	16	23	30	

SEPTEMBER

M		7	14	21	28
Tu	1	8	15	22	29
W	2	9	16	23	30
Th	3	10	17	24	
F	4	11	18	25	
Sa	5	12	19	26	
Su	6	13	20	27	

OCTOBER

M		5	12	19	26
Tu		6	13	20	27
W		7	14	21	28
Th	1	8	15	22	29
F	2	9	16	23	30
Sa	3	10	17	24	31
Su	4	11	18	25	

NOVEMBER

M		2	9	16	23	30
Tu		3	10	17	24	
W		4	11	18	25	
Th		5	12	19	26	
F		6	13	20	27	
Sa		7	14	21	28	
Su	1	8	15	22	29	

DECEMBER

M		7	14	21	28
Tu	1	8	15	22	29
W	2	9	16	23	30
Th	3	10	17	24	31
F	4	11	18	25	
Sa	5	12	19	26	
Su	6	13	20	27	

RELAX & UNWIND

Beware the

*Writer Valerie McConnell and **Yours** readers remember those scary fibs that kept us quaking in our boots...*

Many, many years ago, facing the scary transition from Infants to Juniors, I lived with an additional, secret, fear. A big boy across the road told me that in junior school you had to do 100 sums every day and if you got any of them wrong they cut you up and served you for school dinner. Sums weren't my strong point – making it even more frightening.

It seems big boys can be cruel to the young and old, as **Mary Archer** remembers... "At the bottom of the school lane was a large area of thick undergrowth. The older boys in our group told us about an old man who lived there in a caravan, called by everyone 'Old Daddy Masher'.

"The boys would bang on the side of his home and throw rocks onto the roof. He would come out holding a large knobbly stick and shout incomprehensible words at us. The boys told us girls that if he caught you, he would drag you inside and put you into his large, black cooking pot.

"When cooked, we would be mashed up as food for his huge dog. My legs shook for ages afterwards from the very fast run home. We believed every word and were quite petrified. He was probably a poor old soldier who had served this country during the war but had come from far away –

which was why we couldn't understand him. Houses have since been built there and I like to think he was rehoused in a more suitable and much warmer home."

Big girls could be mean too, of course – although at least some got their comeuppance. "I was terrorised by two girls a bit older than me at junior school," writes **Margaret Phillips.** "One especially always threatened to take me from my home on a Saturday morning and hang me from her apple tree! I always made sure I was out somewhere on Saturday mornings. Years later I recognised her when I was working in a chemist's shop. I made her wait ages for her prescription."

Apples had a role to play in **Susan Grey's** story. "One day while playing in the street, I was eating an apple when one of the 'big girls' came up to me and told me that if I ate the apple core, the pips would take root and an apple tree would grow inside me. I handed the core over to her and she gobbled it up, laughing.

"A few weeks later I heard that this girl was ill in bed with tummy problems. Apparently she had regularly been eating other girls' apple cores. And while the pips hadn't taken root, they do contain cyanide and in great numbers are harmful to the human system.*"

Irene Roberts' childhood terrors, though, were just down to too much imagination... "My sleepless night came from a chalked message I saw on our gable-end wall one windy winter evening. THE GHOST WALKS TONIGHT! I was terror-stricken and can still remember vividly how I slept with my head under the blankets that night. Needless to say, the ghost didn't walk and I found out years later that it meant it was pay-day."

But some people, who should know better, were quite happy to terrify us into obedience, whether it concerned undesirable sweets or bedtime. Step forward mums and grans... "When we were children," emails **Margaret Reynolds,** "Our mother used to tell us that the rag and bone man collected all the rubbish and boiled it up in a big vat. The liquid was drained off to make liquorice, which we called 'Spanish juice' and the solid remains were minced up and made into chewing gum!"

S Murkett's gran was no better: "How well I remember my gran telling my sister and me if we didn't go to bed when told, the nine-o-clock horses would come. We were scared to death. She also told us if we didn't go to school the blue man would come knocking on the door. We were always on the lookout for that scary blue man."

bogeyman

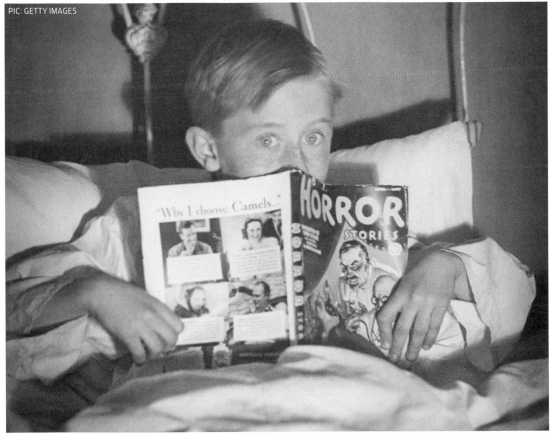

PIC: GETTY IMAGES

So it's nice to report that confessing to a grown-up can bring a happy ending...
"When I was six, my brother and sister teased me, saying I was adopted and had been found on the doorstep," writes **Patricia Knight.** "They said I was Chinese really and my dark, basin-cut hair and slanted eyes proved it. I did cry, but daren't ask my mum in case it was true.

"That night I was woken with terrible pain and the doctor was called. He was a fierce, elderly gentlemen, but Mum said he was always right. That made it worse for me because as soon as he saw me he said, 'Hello my little China doll". I burst into tears and cried the whole time he was checking me over. He told Mum I had yellow jaundice and made a quick exit.

"Mum said he was embarrassed by my silly tears. Hours later he appeared in my room and carried me downstairs. He apologised for upsetting me and gave me a half-pound bar of chocolate.

"Mum made me tell her what had caused my tears and though relieved it wasn't the doctor, was upset about my brother and sister's behaviour.

"As a punishment she said they couldn't have any chocolate. We didn't have much chocolate in 1959, so you can imagine how great it was to have all that to myself. My siblings were green with envy!"

*Susan is right and apple pips do contain a form of cyanide, but the amount you would have to eat is so large, that it's unlikely this was the problem - even if it seemed a fit punishment!

Given no clue numbers or black squares, can you solve this crossword? When the puzzle is complete, the pattern of the black squares will be wholly symmetrical. This means that you are able to deduce the positions of several more squares right away!

Across
1 Task
4 Extinguish (a fire) (3, 3)
7 Sun-dried brick
8 Goldie - - -, Overboard actress
9 Way out
11 Tragic king
12 Acquired dexterity
15 Rugby forward
16 Greek god
19 Member of an early conquering people of parts of England
21 Position taken up for a photographer
23 A distance away
24 Destitute
25 Short sharp karate blow
27 Type of music associated with Ella Fitzgerald
28 Surrender

Puzzles

30 Unclothed
31 Rim
34 Yorkshire valley
36 Complete trust
38 Metal fixing pin
39 Authentic
40 Saudi person?
41 Restriction
42 Attain by threat
43 Determined attempt

Down
1 Develop naturally
2 Gelatine obtained from seaweed
3 Damp and cold
4 Quick, furtive glance
5 Excursion
6 Alcoholic beverage
8 Saintly circlet
10 Threesome
13 Neighbouring
14 Enclosure for chickens
17 Rascal, scoundrel
18 Impudence
19 Beauty parlour
20 Wanderer
21 Award
22 Wasp's weapon
26 Father
27 Joke
28 Snuggle up to
29 Stupid fellow
32 Gloomy and dingy
33 Join (armed forces)
35 Hence
36 Pressed woollen fabric
37 Detest
38 Unstylish, inferior

Were you right? Turn to page 182 for the answers

ROUND AND ABOUT

Each clue's answer appears in the box, starting in its numbered square and moving in a zigzag path horizontally or vertically, but not diagonally. The last letter of each answer is the first letter of the next, but other letters are used only once. To make things a bit trickier, we've left four clue numbers out of the grid. The first word is already marked.

1 Motley or unkempt (6-6)
2 Part-time host of This Morning (6, 6)
3 Treat superficially (7, 3, 7)
4 In all directions (5, 5, 3)
5 Arabian republic (5)
6 Area or locality (4, 2, 3, 5)
7 Wild guess (4, 2, 3, 4)
8 Percussion instrument (10)
9 Chestnuts cooked in syrup (7, 6)
10 Coronation Street character (5, 7)
11 The - - -, sixth novel by Thomas Hardy (6, 2, 3, 6)
12 Christian festival (6)
13 German white wine (8)
14 Lord of the Rings character (7)
15 Pay the whole cost (4, 3, 4)
16 With a carefree manner (5-9)

L	F	T	T	B	I	R	A	G	G	L	A	G
A	O	O	H	E	L	L	H	T	H	E	T	G
D	N	R	U	H	T	I	G	Y	E	A	E	L
G	A	F	S	E	H	C	T	L	D	R	A	M
N	I	A	C	E	R	Y	A	R	E	T	N	O
S	L	E	T	V	E	W	H	C	S	E	N	H
E	I	R	S	M	U	R	I	W	A	M	L	O
I	V	E	A	A	R	D	C	H	Y	E	O	F
T	R	U	T	O	R	E	L	T	E	M	K	T
A	N	R	E	N	L	A	E	T	N	E	C	H
N	O	E	T	S	G	C	K	R	O	H	S	E
E	F	B	S	L	L	E	D	A	T	I	D	W
H	T	E	W	Y	A	S	E	H	T	N	O	O

A Year With **Yours** 2020   151

A sense of

The circle of life can help bring new meaning

"Here you go, Mum." My daughter handed me a mug of coffee. "Thank you," I said, stirring in two sugars.

It felt wrong her waiting on me. A role reversal I couldn't get used to and one that made me feel rather useless. I was staying at her lovely townhouse for a few days and watched as she tidied the front room.

She'd never shown the remotest interest in anything domestic growing up. We'd fallen out many times about the state of her bedroom, but now she seemed perfectly at ease.

I followed her through to the kitchen, thinking I could help her cook dinner, but she shooed me away with a smile. "Go and sit down, Mum," she said, with an affectionate smile.

"Try to relax." I drifted away, wishing briefly I was at home with John, walking through the fields behind our house, or reading in front of the fire, but my husband wasn't there, and the house felt too big without him.

When Grace had invited me to visit I jumped at the chance, but being around her only highlighted how narrow my life had become since retiring from teaching. I was even more set in my ways than before, hardly veering from my self-imposed routines.

John had lost patience a while ago, accusing me of no longer being the woman he'd married – the one who used to laugh a lot, and loved an adventure – but I hadn't been that woman for years.

When Grace was five we lost a baby boy, and it had brought home to me how horribly fragile life was. My controlling behaviour had become a way of holding uncertainty at bay, but as she grew older Grace had started to rebel. She'd left home early, gone travelling to places where I couldn't get hold of her, and hooked up with unsuitable boys. I grew more and more anxious, more rigid in my ways, praying that one day she'd come back to me.

And now here she was, transformed by love, happily settled at last. Matthew had been a wonderful surprise; the kind of son-in-law I'd dreamed of, but had thought she'd never meet.

I could hear her singing in the kitchen, and marvelled at how easily she'd taken to married life. She took after her father, thank goodness, and was stronger in ways I'd never been.

A cry from the room above made my heart leap, and brought me out of my reverie. I moved into the hall and ran up the stairs, the years falling away, and in the nursery I gazed at my grandson in his cradle.

He smiled, and I plucked him out and pressed him to my shoulder, inhaling his delicious, soft, sweet infant scent.

"Hello, Alfie," I murmured. "It's time for his lunch," said Grace behind me. Her face was gentle, and my heart brimmed with love.

"Would you like to feed him?"

"Yes, please."

We went downstairs, Grace handed me his bottle, and as I cradled him in my arms, watching

---

"When Grace was five we lost a baby boy and it brought home to me how horribly fragile life was"

---

his eyelids flutter, a sense of purpose flowed through me.

But I knew it wasn't enough. I couldn't rely on Grace and Alfie to fill my life with meaning. I had to learn from my past mistakes.

"Why don't you accompany Dad the next time he goes on a trip?" Grace said, keeping her eyes on Alfie.

"He doesn't mind travelling alone, Mum, but he'd prefer it if you went with him."

"I know," I said, quietly.

It was something I'd considered before Alfie was born, knowing it had been John's dream for us to go travelling when we retired. But now little Alfie was here, how could I bear to leave? It was hard enough, living right at the other end

BY KAREN CLARK

purpose

of the country.

"We'll be here, waiting," Grace said, as if she'd read my mind. Her eyes met mine: a smoky grey, like her father's. She stroked Alfie's head, then rested her hand on mine.

"Think of all the stories you'll have to tell your grandson."

I studied him, my vision blurring, and imagined the bond we might have one day if I was lucky, then turned to Grace and smiled at her through my flowing tears.

"I don't suppose you have a suitcase I can borrow?" I said.

153

Lipstick, powder

Writer Valery McConnell and **Yours** *readers remember the magic of make-up, with Max Factor, Miners and co...*

I know that everybody is supposed to remember their first kiss, but I think the first item of make-up you own is just as unforgettable (and probably more fun!).

Angela Patchett has never forgotten hers... "In 1954, my best friend gave me, aged 14, my very first Max Factor compact. It was winter and I went into the school toilets and covered my red nose in the powder, but I was caught by the gym mistress who made me wash my face.

"After that I only wore it at weekends when I would also paint my lips with bright red lipstick. Max Factor was advertised as the make-up for film stars so it always made me feel glamorous." Quite right. Red lips, a powder compact and film-star glamour sums up the Fifties look.

How things had changed when I was making my first make-up purchase near the end of the Sixties. Anybody remember Rimmel's Hide 'n' Heal? Shaped like a push-up lipstick, you rubbed it over your teenage spots in a brave attempt at a flawless complexion. And because it was sold as 'medicated' – I could tell my dad, who like many a father didn't want his 13-year-old daughter sporting "war paint", that it was spot cream.

What I didn't tell him was that it also worked to give you the super-pale lips which were very trendy then.

I wasn't the only one who hankered to look like Twiggy (above) and co - huge black eyes and pale, pale faces. **Vicki Clohessy** was having a mini-rebellion too: "My best friend Hazel and I were fresh out of grammar school in the mid-Sixties and thought ourselves very 'with it'.

"Miners did black-and-white nail varnish complete with transfers, so we had alternate black and white nails on each hand with contrasting transfers. We wore lots of black eyeliner and mascara and drew long black lashes under our lower eyelids.

"She had white boots, I had black so we wore one of each. I had a PVC mac that had four large black and white squares on the front and Hazel had a shiny black PVC mac. We used to go out like that - and got strange looks from passers by - but most people just smiled at us. Those were the days!"

And the brand most used to create those heavy Sixties lashes? The same one that Angela had been using in the Fifties. Max Factor's block mascara was mentioned time and again by **Yours** readers, including **Lynn Ryding**... "I was 18 in 1963 and my strongest memory is the blocks of black mascara you would spit in and mix in a gloop with the little brush before sweeping on your lashes.

"We used to draw our lashes underneath our eyes with a pencil or eyeliner brush. My friend Rosie could do it perfectly while mine were wobbly. We thought we were the bees' knees unless it rained when everything would run as nothing was waterproof in those days."

Janet Ridley's lash routine was painstaking – almost literally. "Between each layer of mascara I would carefully pat on powder for maximum lash build-up. Then I would take a pin and separate any clumps. I was lucky I didn't poke my eye out.

"I'd go off to the youth club thinking I looked fabulous. But after an hour or so dancing to Tamla Motown records a visit to

and paint

the toilet would reveal a row of black smudged dots under each eye. Mascara overload!"

Why couldn't make-up ever stay where it was supposed to?

"When I was about 16 I used to plaster on a thick layer of pan stick, covered with face powder," writes **Rosemary Medland**. "I thought I looked marvellous, until my then-boyfriend complained he went home with half of it on the shoulder of his best jacket!"

And where did most of us buy our first make-up? Woolies, of course. When budgets were tight Woolworth's counter was the go-to place for Rimmel, Miners, Outdoor Girl and of course its own long-running budget

range – Evette. It was cheap but, frankly, a bit old hat.

Then Woolworth's gave us our very own make-up, as **Brenda Hendley** remembers. "Working as a Saturday girl in Woolworths in the late Sixties, I was lucky enough to be on the make-up counter when they launched Baby Doll Cosmetics.

"As a 15-year-old girl, this range was so exciting. It had lilac, green and blue nail varnish, brown eyeshadow and pale pink, lilac and peach lipsticks, instead of the usual red and orange nail colours worn by our mothers.

"Even the posters were exciting, with illustrated dolly girls in the arms of handsome

men. To my mother's horror, I went out that weekend sporting lilac nail polish and lilac lipstick to match my lilac mini dress. I can still remember how excited and glamorous I felt."

But what goes on, must come off. You hope, anyway...
"I remember poring over the make-up counter at Woolworths," emails **Heather Moulson**. "The day finally came when I could buy a Miners Chelsea Chick lipstick of frosty pink. I should have left it at that. However, I just had to have the magenta eyeshadow that was liquid and went on with a brush. Three days that took to come off! I was very red-eyed indeed!"

Cold Calling

When it comes to telemarketing, it's all about your sales pitch...

"Can I interest you in some raffle tickets?" Viola asked the woman on the other end of the telephone. "They're £10 each or three for £25 and–"

"No," the woman said.

Viola could picture the grim set of the woman's mouth, the stiffening of her shoulders. This would be an almost impossible sale. But she'd been around long enough to know all the tricks, all the psychology, and she wasn't about to be put off so easily.

"It's for a well-known children's charity: Kids are Precious," Viola continued. "I'm sure you'd have heard of it."

"No I don't want any tickets."

Keep her talking. "The first prize is a weekend for two at a heavenly hotel in your home city, including breakfast, which is a wonderful added bonus, I think you'll agree."

"I've just told you–"

"Considering what hotels charge for breakfast, it's a fantastic deal," Viola insisted. "There are only 500 tickets in the raffle, so your chances of winning are high."

Experience told her that any second now the other woman would slam down her phone. She couldn't let that happen – these tickets had to be sold. "If you're not willing to buy raffle tickets, would you be interested in selling some to help sick children?"

A huff of disbelief came down the line. "No!"

"You don't want to help sick kiddies? That's a bit shocking. You sound so nice too, like a person who really cares. A book only has 10 tickets, so you just have to make three sales at £25 and one at £10."

"I can't believe we're having this conversation."

Believe it. Viola looked at the books of tickets she still had to offload. If she could keep this woman talking a little bit longer she'd surely wear her down. That was how it generally worked. There were courses dedicated to this type of cold selling. The mantra was: Don't let your target off the hook. And she wasn't about to let this fish swim free.

"I'll get into trouble for saying this, but I can't hold it back," Viola said with an ocean of tears

BY VICTORIA CHIE

in her voice. "My son's very sick. He's one of the children who could be helped by any donation you'd be kind enough to make." She caught her breath, as if swallowing heartbreak. "That's why I volunteered to do this."

"I'm sorry you're in that situation..." The other woman's voice trailed off.

Viola could almost feel her target's discomfort flowing down the line, the guilt she was feeling for being so callous.

That story about a sick son was a pack of lies, of course. She didn't have any kids. But everything was fair in war and cold calling – or so she'd always believed.

"The doctors are trying everything for my son," Viola said. "But there's never enough money for equipment or research. With the economy the way it is, the government can only do so much. And it's little kiddies that suffer." She blew her nose and did some snuffling that could have won her an Oscar.

"You poor thing. What's wrong with your son?"

Experience told her that any second now the other woman would slam down her phone. She couldn't let that happen – these tickets had to be sold

---

Viola blew her nose again to give herself time to come up with something suitably exotic.

"That sounds a dreadful disease," the woman replied.

"It is – and it's rare." Viola glanced at the clock on the wall, willing the woman to surrender. "Even if you only buy one ticket it would be much appreciated by Kids are Precious."

"I'll take two. You're very persuasive."

"Thank you so much. And good luck. I hope you win."

After she'd taken the woman's details Viola walked back to her kitchen and turned down the heat on the peas, which had started to boil over.

"Who was that ringing?" her husband Phil asked.

"A call centre trying to sell us home

Short story

improvements." He rolled his eyes and looked annoyed. "Why didn't you hang up?"

"I wanted to give them a taste of their own medicine for a change." Viola smiled at the memory. "Can you believe it? I sold two whole tickets."

Phil made a grunting noise. "Maybe you're in the wrong job."

"I'm counting on them taking our number off the list."

He was about to say something when the phone in the living room jangled to life.

"Right on time," Viola said. "I'm ready to mash the potatoes, so I reckon it's another nuisance call."

"Ignore it"

"Are you kidding?" She grabbed a bundle of tickets and hurried towards the phone. "I've still got heaps more of these to sell."

HIDE 'N' SEEK WORDSEARCH

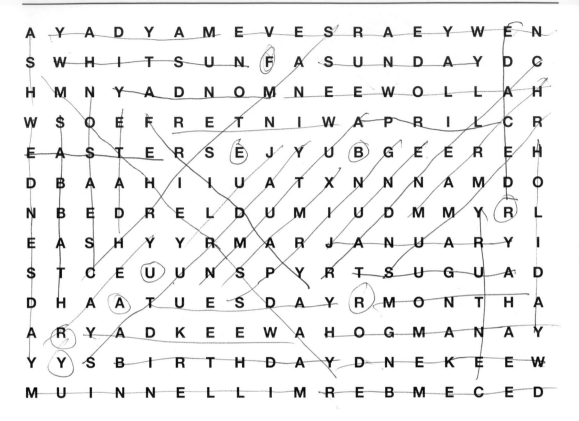

```
A Y A D Y A M E V E S R A E Y W E N
S W H I T S U N F A S U N D A Y D C
H M N Y A D N O M N E E W O L L A H
W S O E F R E T N I W A P R I L C R
E A S T E R S E J Y U B G E E R E H
D B A A H I U A T X N N N A M D O
N B E D R E L D U M I U D M M Y R L
E A S H Y Y R M A R J A N U A R Y I
S T C E U U N S P Y R T S U G U A D
D H A A T U E S D A Y R M O N T H A
A R Y A D K E E W A H O G M A N A Y
Y Y S B I R T H D A Y D N E K E E W
M U I N N E L L I M R E B M E C E D
```

This hide 'n' seek about the calendar is sure to make your day! Take your time finding all of the listed words in the grid, then use some of the remaining letters to spell out another related word

APRIL	HALLOWEEN	SABBATH
ASH WEDNESDAY	HOGMANAY	SATURDAY
AUGUST	HOLIDAY	SEASON
AUTUMN	JANUARY	SPRING
BIRTHDAY	JULY	SUMMER
CALENDAR	JUNE	SUNDAY
CENTURY	MARCH	TUESDAY
CHRISTMAS	MAY DAY	WEEKDAY
DATE	MILLENNIUM	WEEKEND
DECADE	MONDAY	WHITSUN
DECEMBER	MONTH	WINTER
EASTER	MOTHER'S DAY	XMAS
FRIDAY	NEW YEAR'S EVE	YEAR

February (handwritten)

KNIGHT MOVES

Each clue's answer appears in the grid, starting at its numbered square and going to the next letter by way of a chess knight's move. The last letter of each answer is the first letter of the next answer — with the last letter of 10 being the first of 1. All other letters are used only once. A knight in chess can move one square across and two up or down. So, in the diagram below, a knight on the marked centre could move to any of the pink squares.

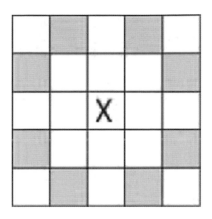

1   Canadian singer who had a no 1 hit with My Heart Will Go On (6, 4)
2   British word for 'diapers' (7)
3   Country formerly known as Ceylon (3, 5)
4   US state which is home to the Grand Canyon (7)
5   Britain's only venomous snake (5)
6   Blind singer and pianist whose hits include Hit the Road Jack (3, 7)
7   Group whose Merry Xmas Everybody is heard every yuletide (5)
8   - - - Scissorhands, 1990 film starring Johnny Depp and Winona Ryder (6)
9   TV presenter whose interviews with Richard Nixon were the subject of a 2008 film (5, 5)
10 - - - of Capricorn, imaginary line south of the equator (6)

L	D	C	R	R	V	A	E
H	I	R	I	Y	³S	A	A
F	E	A	O	O	⁹D	I	⁶R
L	A	R	E	N	P	S	W
⁷S	¹C	²N	⁴A	I	N	E	P
O	R	D	E	A	K	D	¹⁰T
I	L	Z	⁵A	O	D	I	D
I	N	P	A	L	D	R	⁸E

Were you right? Turn to page 182 for the answers

Hooked on

Patience is a virtue learned in a lifetime...

"Here she comes," the assistant announced. Anne quickly put away her crochet. Not quite quickly enough.

Carole laughed. "That's how I'll always think of you mum, putting away your crochet."

"Whereas when I think of you I have so many different pictures in my head." Many of them places I've sat waiting for you, she could have added. She studied her daughter in her wedding dress. She'd known Carole would look wonderful and wasn't disappointed. "This will be a favourite, though?"

"It looks good, doesn't it?"

"Perfect. Absolutely perfect."

As Carole changed, the assistant gave Anne a length of thin ribbon she'd used to trim the dress. Again, she didn't quite have it packed away before her daughter could see.

It was a real sign Carole was now grown up that she didn't roll her eyes as Anne packed away her work. She wasn't more patient, just more tactful. "What are you making anyway? You never said."

"You'll find out soon enough."

"I hope it is soon."

Anne just smiled. She'd learned to crochet during the last few weeks she was pregnant with Carole. It had been a hot sultry summer and Anne was restless and eager to have the birth over.

Her mother-in-law had advised, "you'd be best off learning to enjoy waiting, I'll teach you to crochet."

Learning to handle the hook and wool had distracted Anne for a while and stopped her fretting. By the time Carole was born she'd produced one neat square, and a few weird shaped ones! She discovered the hook was the ideal thing to carry in her handbag so she could make the most of any free moments. At first there was few of those, but Anne created another square when baby Carole had a fever and Anne sat with her through the night.

She made another while Carole spent her first morning at school without her mum, and one after

Carole fell out of a tree and had an operation to set the bone in her arm. One way or another Anne had spent a lot of time waiting for her daughter.

As Anne's skill with the hook increased she incorporated different materials. One square was made using a strip of Carole's comfort blanket. She used the trim from her first party dress and her school uniform. Various hair ribbons were also incorporated. Anne crocheted as Carole took her

---

All of the squares she had made so far were laid out in Carole's old bedroom and neatly stitched together

---

exams, went on her first date and took her driving test. She made another the night Carole and Liam were engaged. That one was made from strands of a carrier bag from the shop where they'd met and had been really tricky to work. Anne backed the square with cloth as she didn't think the plastic alone would hold much heat.

All of the squares she had made so far were laid out in Carole's old bedroom and neatly stitched together. Just three more were needed to complete the blanket she'd give Carole when the time was right. One square would be made from a combination of the ribbon she'd just collected and the blue silk Liam's wedding waistcoat was made from. Another would be made using trimming from their wedding gifts and party favours. The final one wouldn't be Anne's responsibility.

On the day, just over a year later, Anne learned she was to become a grandmother, she gave Carole the beautiful blanket of crocheted squares and a photo album. Each page of the album corresponded to a square on the blanket. Most pages held a photo of Carole, details of what she was doing at the time and an explanation of the materials. The first page showed Anne's scan from

BY KAREN CLARK

a feeling

when she was carrying Carole. The square was made from the same delicate pink wool as her gran, Anne's mother-in-law, had used for her christening shawl.

"This is fantastic, Mum! It must've taken years."

"A lifetime!" she quipped, explaining she'd made a square every time she waited for her.

"Now I understand why I've seen you using your hook so often!"

"It's not really mine. It was your grandmother's and now it's yours." She indicated the final blank space.

"Can you teach me now? I can't wait to see it finished.

"You'll have to wait, at least until I can buy suitable wool." Anne would take her time selecting the perfect yarn for the shawl she would make the baby. She'd take her time teaching Carole to crochet, too, although it would be the baby's job to teach her patience.

When things were

*Writer Valery McConnell and **Yours** readers remember the long-lived everyday items and their past links...*

Even better than family heirlooms are those everyday items from our childhood that we still use today. In our house, that's my late mother-in-law's breadboard – 80 years old at least – and pudding spoons that were a wedding present to my parents. As I eat my blueberries and healthy yogurt, they bring back memories of tinned fruit and evaporated milk, banana custard and jelly and ice-cream.

Talking of jelly, **Mrs Wright** has just made her first great-grandson a blancmange bunny in the glass mould her mother used during the war...

"My memories of a cream or chocolate bunny with chopped-up green jelly round the edges for grass and currants for eyes are still with me vividly!"

It must be around the same age as **Sandy Oliver's**: "My jelly mould was bought by my gran in 1932 and blancmange and jelly rabbits are now a firm favourite with adults and children alike at family gatherings."

But not all treats had to be sweet. "During the war," emails **Doris Turrell**, "my mother used to bring hot stew in patterned china bowls down the garden for my brother and I while we sheltered from V1s, V2s, and rockets in the Anderson shelter. Every time I use them now I recall having our stew in these bowls."

The best pudding memories can be savoury too. "I still use the dessert spoon my mum did when beating her Yorkshire puddings," emails **Pat Butler**. "It's worn on the left side due to 'rubbing' on the side of the dish. She died in 1989 and although I don't make Yorkshires as often as she did, it's a happy reminder of her when I do."

Glenda Wells has a rather special spoon too. "My father was born in 1926 and his baby feeding spoon (see picture right) has since been used as a sugar spoon. It has now passed down to me and is still used every day."

But some items go back generations...

Christine Jefferies is still using a rolling pin, "that belonged to my father's grandmother – and he was born in 1900."

Margaret Watson, likewise, has a fork (see right) that belonged to her grandfather's family and he was born in 1887. "One disadvantage – it doesn't go in the dishwasher!" You can't have everything Margaret. "My grandfather acquired a

Cross and Blackwell tin opener from a neighbour before the Second World War," emails **Andrew Redding**. "It's still in our family (see above) and a quick check online shows it was patented in 1881."

But the longevity prize goes to **Mary Gruber's** ice-cream scoop, "More than 130 years old and still giving good service. It belonged to my mother's aunt, who kept a confectionery shop in the 19th Century (my mother was born in 1896). It works much better than present-day ones and I shall pass it on to my daughter."

Let's hear it for the stove-top heroes of the kitchen...

"I am still using my late mother's egg poacher," writes **Joyce Hodge**. "Bought from Woolworths in the Twenties, I use it every week and it has been on gas, electric, radiant rings and once, in a power cut, on the open fire. I also have a twisted wire ring for getting boiled eggs out of water."

Christine Burden is the proud possessor of her

made to last

mother's porringer - which she acquired in the Thirties. "It's the one item I would never part with. It's great for making porridge, melting chocolate and scrambling eggs."

Mrs Sharp still has her four-pint teapot bought in 1959, the year she was married.

"We used it when our many friends called round for a cuppa, but it's not been used for some time - not since we discovered wine..."

Julie Atack's potato peeler is 55... How down the years, she has not accidentally thrown it in the bin with the peelings, I don't know. "It has a single blade with string wound round the handle so there is nothing to break," she writes.

Honor Day (83), writes, "For my 21st birthday, my mum bought me a pink plastic brush and comb set. It cost 2/6. I've used it every day of my life and it hasn't lost one tooth or bristle."

Sylvia Monk's 40-year-old Mother's Day gift is a Blue Peter inspired jewellery box her children made with their late grandmother. Yes, stickyback plastic and matchboxes. "I still use it for keeping my earrings in and it holds together as well as the day it was made!"

Kitchen aid

An offer of help is meant in the kindest way, but is she up to the task?

"Stand back, everyone," Emma said. Her trio of assistants moved well away from the oven. Emma pulled the door open a little way, allowing a faint waft of delicious-smelling steam to escape, before opening it fully.

She basted the roasting meat and turned the potatoes. Both were already looking close to ready. Her mouth watered. She hadn't cooked a proper Sunday dinner in a long time. There just hadn't been time.

Her girls were at school now, but the youngest only went for the mornings, so dropping them off and going back twice in the day to collect them took up almost as much time as they spent in lessons.

Then there had been Mum's new hip. The operation had gone well. So had the alterations to her flat; a higher toilet seat, shower cubicle where a bath had been, and a new armchair. That meant she'd be able to cope just fine on her own once she felt ready for that. Arranging it all, as well as the hospital visiting, had taken up a lot of Emma's

---

It would've been quicker to do the job herself but she knew the girls loved helping her. It built their confidence and they'd learn to be useful in time

---

time though.

"Can I help, Mum?" a little voice piped up to ask.

"Thanks, love." Emma gave her eldest some carrots and showed her how to use the peeler. It would've been quicker to do the job herself but she knew the girls loved helping her. It built up their confidence and they'd learn to be useful in time.

Next Emma whisked up Yorkshire pudding batter and put it in the fridge, just like her Mum had taught her. Then, unlike she'd been taught,

she opened a tin of rice pudding to use for the Queen of Puddings dessert she had planned and began spooning it into a dish.

"Can I help?"

"Yes love, thank you - fetch me an egg, will you, please?"

"All gone, Mummy."

"There's a new box in the fridge."

After some rummaging, Emma heard, "Can't find it."

Just as she put down the tin and spoon, she remembered. "Oh, that's right. We had scrambled eggs for tea last night." Now what was she going to do for dessert? Queen of Puddings without meringue topping was just rice and jam; perfectly OK, but not what they'd all been drooling over.

An eager voice chimed in, "I could go to the shop and buy more?"

It was on the tip of Emma's tongue to say no, but she stopped herself. She remembered going to the shop for Mum when she was little, and how proud she'd felt to be trusted and useful to her. It was so important for people to feel a sense of that, no matter what their age.

Eggs were eggs: it'd be very hard to get the job wrong. The shop wasn't far away. If Emma walked there by herself it took less than five minutes. Her would-be helper wouldn't do it quite so quickly, but she'd get there and back in time for the pudding to be hastily assembled and put in the oven to brown while they ate the main course. Running the errand would actually be pretty useful, too.

"I do know not to talk to strangers."

Emma grinned. "I know you do."

Of course she did. It was something Emma had learned from her mum and passed on to her kids. Should Emma let her go?

Eyes, almost the mirror of hers, pleaded that she should.

"And I know how to get there…"

She should do, as they'd all walked down there

BY PATSY COLLINS

quite often, and just the day before. Emma had held her hand then, though. Letting her go alone was so different, and naturally Emma felt responsible for her. But she knew she could walk that far, eggs weren't too heavy for her to carry, and she should be able to complete the

task without difficulty. There wasn't even a road to cross.

"Please let me. I'm going to have to learn to do things for myself sometime, you know."

"Learn? You're the one who taught me. Thanks, Mum. If you don't mind going, it'll be a help."

A RIGHT ROYAL MESS

Read the story and using the grid to record any positive facts with a tick and any negative facts with a cross. You should then be able to work out more as you cross-refer the facts.

	Queen					Century					Kitchen foul-up				
	Edith	Edna	Edwina	Elfrida	Ethel	Seventh century	Eighth century	Ninth century	Tenth century	Eleventh century	Custard lumpy	Egg too hard	Porridge stuck	Runny pancake	Soufflé fell
Edgar															
Edmund															
Edred															
Edward															
Edwy															
Custard lumpy										
Egg too hard										
Porridge stuck										
Runny pancake										
Soufflé fell										
Seventh century					
Eighth century					
Ninth century					
Tenth century					
Eleventh century					

Were you right? Turn to page 182 for the answers

The story of King Alfred and how he burnt the cakes is well known to every schoolchild. What is not known to conventional historians is that there are five other ancient British monarchs who also experienced a culinary disaster to match Alfred's.

Edred, whose soufflé collapsed, was neither the earliest nor the latest of the five kings. Edith was queen to neither Edgar nor the king whose pancake turned out runny, who reigned in the century after Edgar. Edward's queen wasn't Edwina, whose husband produced lumpy custard sometime before the tenth century, whereas Edna proudly sat next to her king Edwy. The little-known incident of the stone-hard boiled egg happened in the tenth century while the 'porridge stuck to the saucepan' catastrophe didn't occur in the following century. Edmund ascended the throne during the eighth century and 100 years later the incumbent king was supported admirably by his queen, Ethel.

Can you match the right queen to each king, establish in which century he reigned and what the culinary foul-up was?

KING	QUEEN	CENTURY	KITCHEN FOUL-UP

CRISS CROSS

Can you put in a shockingly good performance with this criss cross on electrical items that you plug in?

3 LETTERS
FAN
FAX
SAW

4 LETTERS
FIRE
IRON
LAMP
PUMP

TILL

5 LETTERS
CLOCK
DRILL
KNIFE
MIXER
MOWER
RADIO
TONGS

6 LETTERS
COOKER
FRIDGE
ICEBOX
SANDER
SCALES
SHAVER
STEREO
SUN BED
VACUUM

7 LETTERS
BLANKET
BLENDER
FREEZER
JUKEBOX

PRINTER
SCANNER
TOASTER

8 LETTERS
CHAINSAW
STRIMMER
TEASMADE
TRAIN SET

9 LETTERS
HAIRDRYER
MICROWAVE
TIN-OPENER

10 LETTERS
CALCULATOR

PERCOLATOR

11 LETTERS
ANSWERPHONE
COFFEE MAKER
HEDGE CUTTER
PHOTOCOPIER

12 LETTERS
FRUIT MACHINE
PHONE CHARGER
POPCORN MAKER

15 LETTERS
KNITTING
MACHINE

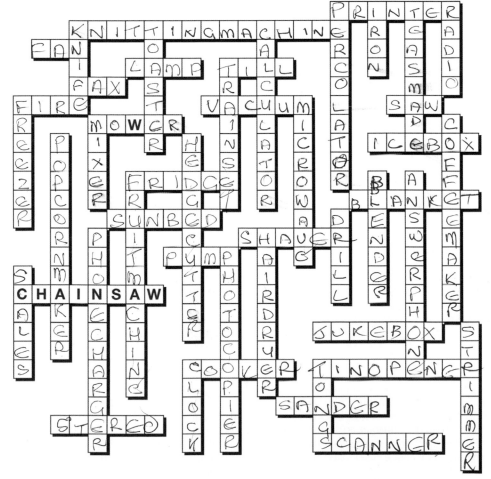

Retro perspective

Life was much better in the Fifties...wasn't it?

Monica had never coveted the role of housewife. She was proud to be a full-time working woman, refusing to employ the skills her grandmother had taught her, and was taken aback when her mother-in-law gave her a book called The Fifties Housewife for the Modern Woman for her birthday.

"My son deserves better," she said with a sniff. She'd never forgiven Monica for getting married in red. "He could do with a square meal - look how skinny he's getting."

"That's because he's taken up running." Monica said, but Andrew looked rather delighted.

"Why not give it a whirl?" he suggested, and Monica could tell he was picturing an apple pie, just like Mother used to make. He flipped through the book, frowning. "On second thoughts, it sounds like hard work."

Snatching the book from him Monica read out loud, "The Goal: Try to make your home a place of peace and order where your husband can renew himself in body and spirit." What about my body and spirit? She wondered, but something inside her stirred. She couldn't resist a challenge. "OK I'll give it a go," she said.

She booked a long-overdue fortnight off work and threw herself into the role as housewife. She wasn't trying to impress anyone - least of all her mother-in-law - but she wanted to prove she could do it.

So there she was, in an apron and full make-up, peeling spuds and whizzing around with a feather duster. In the spirit of things she'd been laying out Andrew's clothes at bedtime, and making sandwiches for him to take to work. She spoke in a soothing voice at all times - as instructed in The Book - and stopped expressing opinions. In the evenings they played board games.

"This is wonderful," Andrew said, at the end of the first week. Being waited on clearly suited him. "Our roles are properly defined for a change, don't you think?" Monica handed him his beer and kept smiling. Housewives of the Fifties weren't supposed to bash their husbands over the head.

"How's it going?" her friend Susan said, dropping round for coffee. She looked around. "It looks fantastic."

"I'm shattered," Monica said, flopping in an armchair.

Admittedly, it was satisfying cooking meals from scratch and she and Andrew felt better for it, but baking cakes, ironing sheets and putting fresh flowers out each day meant Monica was too tired for conversation in the evenings. "Andrew thinks he's died and gone to heaven - and his mother's over the moon," she grumbled.

"It's a bit extreme," Susan said, flicking through the book. "You're not getting up in the middle of the night to refresh your make-up, are you?"

"Not anymore." Monica said. "I've stopped polishing his shoes, too." She sighed. I feel like the

---

The Goal: Try to make your home a place of peace and order where your husband can renew himself in body and spirit...

---

real me's gone."

"I'm not surprised." Susan looked mildly shocked. "I wouldn't dream of polishing my husband's shoes."

"Andrew told me I wasn't smiling enough last night," Monica said. "It's completely gone to his head."

"If he's so keen on traditional roles, maybe you should take it to the next level," said Susan, meaningfully.

"I've decided to give up work," Monica said chirpily over dinner.

He looked startled. "But I thought you loved your job?"

"I like being at home more," she said pulling out the knitting Susan had cobbled together.

Andrew watched her clicking the needles together. "But we need the money," he said. "What about the mortgage?"

"You'll just have to work harder." She hid a smile at the look of dismay on his face. "What are you doing?" he said later, as she slathered cold cream on her face and popped curlers in her hair.

"'It's my new beauty regimen," she said slipping into a full-length winceyette nightdress and buttoning it up.

BY KAREN CLARK

Looking confused he slithered into bed. "Where's the duvet?" he cried, plucking at the scratchy blankets from a charity shop.

"Didn't use duvets in the Fifties," Monica said cheerfully. "Oh and I'm getting rid of the TV tomorrow." He sat bolt upright in alarm. "I much prefer playing board games."

Things came to a swift conclusion. Andrew realised he preferred the modern Monica, and she definitely preferred him when he wasn't checking the pillow cases for creases.

"You won't be needing that," he said, as she hung up her apron. "Throw it out."

"Actually, I realised I rather like cooking," she confessed, moving in for a hug. "So I've asked your mum to tea."

The birds and

*Writer Valery McConnell and **Yours** readers remember when babies were found under gooseberry bushes...*

For the whole of my last term at primary school, my best friend Joyce and I had only one topic of conversation - how were babies made? And why would nobody tell us?

We had theories on everything, from what the mysterious 'towel' machines on the walls in public loos were, to how babies arrived. I knew they came from the mother's tummy - and as my gran had a very generous cleavage, I assumed that the baby came out from between your breasts.

I prefer the theory told to **Julie Vinsome** though... "At primary school in the Fifties one of the older girls told us how babies were born. 'Ladies who have husbands have a zip that starts at their belly button, and when they want a baby, they just unzip their tummy and the baby jumps out.' I timidly asked if she had a zip. 'Don't be silly,' came the reply. 'I have to get a husband first.'"

Meanwhile, **Pamela Pollock's** friend was hedging her bets: "I was told by a schoolfriend that babies came out of your mummy's tummy button and your mum and dad then gave the baby to the stork to deliver."

Our parents were often the biggest story-tellers, although **Christine Gilbert** remembers it with fondness. "I was born in 1958 and my late mum told me: 'When your dad and I were ready to have a new baby we went to the bottom of a rainbow. We were met by a fairy who took us over the rainbow and let us pick a rose we liked, and you were behind the rose.'

"She said she chose a red rose. I never questioned this and to this day love to think that my mum and dad chose me specially!"

A surprising number of you were fed the gooseberry bush theory, which led **Jean Coughlan** to worry how babies could breathe under the bushes and how they knew when to come out.

Anita Pritchard decided to combine it with that other popular myth, of the baby being brought by the doctor... "Early one morning, when I was six, I was woken up as my new baby brother or sister was arriving.

"I was sure it would be a sister as I really wanted one. I can remember a lot of activity and being kept occupied by my daddy and grandparents.

"Eventually the family doctor came in, held his black bag up and said: 'You've got a new baby brother.' I was convinced the baby was in his bag and that he'd been so long arriving as he had to look under all the gooseberry bushes. I cried and cried and begged him to take him back as I really wanted a sister."

But what about how babies got there in the first place?

Alma Roberts' mum wasn't taking any chances. "My mother said: 'Don't sit next to any men on the bus!' For a long time I thought I might get pregnant that way."

Diane Helmore had to bribe her friend Valerie's big sister Pat with Fry's Five Boys chocolate and flowers to tell them the truth... "but we soon wished we hadn't as this horror story came tumbling from her lips.

"Our eyes popped out as she told us about these rude things that grown-ups did. I knew that my mummy and daddy would never do anything that rude. Then I wondered why Pat would make up such a dreadful story. My childhood ended with that information, but I was determined I would never, ever do that!"

However, sometimes learning the truth goes well - as **Mrs Baker** remembers. "The birds and the bees were a no-go area at school, not even discussed. But the night before our wedding, my mother-in-law handed my husband a book with sealed pages and a brown paper covering. This was for us to take on honeymoon.

"We went to a little caravan in Devon and with great excitement opened the pages. We were shocked to see a naked couple and the title, The Technique of Sex. We did read the book, though, and a few years later we had three children under three!"

the bees

PIC: SHUTTERSTOCK

Dorothy Cullen remembers her friend, who had just had a baby, admitting to her she had to ask her midwife a rather important question when she became pregnant.

"She told me: 'I asked the midwife how does the baby get out of your tummy?' The midwife just said: 'You know how it went in? Well, that's where it comes out!' And she soon found out that this was right."

Even for the royal family? "A few days after my 11th birthday," writes **Mrs Slocombe**, "our headmistress assembled the whole school in the hall. She told us Princess Elizabeth would have her baby very soon. 'If we have a princess you must come to school in the morning and go home at lunchtime. If we have a prince you'll have the whole day off,' she told us. I went home and asked my mother, 'How do they know she'll be having a baby?' 'Oh,' she said, 'they've spotted a stork flying around the palace'. How things have changed."

They certainly have. These days we'd be given the same time off for a prince or a princess - and quite right too!

The forgery

Conning a rogue risks a nasty sting in the tale

BY DELLA GALTON

The bell chimed and Jason glanced up to see a well-dressed woman who was hesitating in the shop doorway.

"Good afternoon. I was wondering if you bought paintings. I have one for sale."

Posh accent, good clothes, but well-worn. Jason would've rubbed his hands together in glee but he didn't want to alarm her.

"Well that depends," he said with a smile. "On what sort of painting it is."

"An original I think - quite valuable, according to my uncle. He left it to me in his Will, God rest his soul." She produced the painting from her cavernous handbag and laid it out on the desk.

It was a racehorse - Jason recognised the distinctive style instantly, and his heartbeat quickened. But he hid his excitement. He pushed his glasses higher on his nose and spent a long time poring over it.

Then he turned to her with a disappointed shake of his head.

"I thought for a moment you had something special, but it's a forgery. You can tell by the signature. Stubbs never signed his name like that."

"Are you sure, dear? I'm certain Uncle wouldn't have been involved in anything illegal."

"It's very good forgery. I'm an expert in forgeries, actually."

Her face fell and she began to wrap the paintings back up.

"That's not to say it's worthless." He rubbed his chin. "there's still a demand for paintings like this - but of course I couldn't pay as much."

"I see..." She looked uncertain and he placed a reassuring hand on her arm.

"Come through to the back and we can discuss this further."

"Thank you, dear." He heard a wobble in her voice. "that's very kind."

Five minutes later they sat in the warmth of the back room. His customer, who'd introduced herself as Grace Harding, glanced at the clutter of objects around them. An antique parrot cage hung from the ceiling and a mirror with a gilt surround stood propped against one wall. They were both nice pieces, but he'd told their erstwhile owners they were good copies. They'd fetch a tidy sum in auction - he wouldn't put them in his shop in case anyone nipped in to check the price tags. You couldn't be too careful these days.

"So how much do you think you could offer me for Uncle's picture?" Grace's quavering voice broke into his thoughts and shattered his reverie.

He frowned and named a figure that was about a tenth of the painting's value.

"I was hoping for a little more." George shook his head in pretended resignation. "I'm sorry, but I have to make a living, you know."

The bell chimed in the shop and he stood up. "Excuse me a moment."

When he returned she was dabbing her eyes. "Are you sure you can't give me anymore?"

In a resigned voice he upped his offer by £40. "But only

Grace counted it carefully on fingers that no longer seemed quite so stiff and arthritic. "God bless you sir," she smile and walked out of his shop at a surprising speed

PIC: SHUTTERSTOCK

because you remind me of my dear old gran." He handed over the money.

Grace counted it carefully on fingers that no longer seemed quite so stiff and arthritic, before squirreling it away in her bag.

"God bless you, sir," she smiled and walked out of his shop at a surprising speed.

He waited until he was sure she was gone before he unwrapped the painting once more.

Hang on! Something wasn't right. Just now he had been struck by its beauty - even the old frame was genuine. But this frame looked tacky and, as he rubbed it, gold flake came off on his fingers.

With a shout he leapt to his feet! Grace Harding - if that was her real name - must have had two paintings in her possession and she had swapped the genuine Stubbs with this crude fake when he'd been seeing to his other customer.

Come to think of it, his other customer had looked familiar. It was the woman who'd sold him the mirror, he realised.

He'd paid her a pittance and she'd obviously been hellbent on revenge! The pair of them must have cooked up this little scam between them. But as it happened, they hadn't got away with it at all.

They might have thought they'd had the last laugh, but it paid to be one step ahead. Jason hadn't lied about one thing. He'd warned Grace Harding he was an expert on forgeries. As she'd no doubt find out when she tried to spend some of the counterfeit cash he had used to pay her...

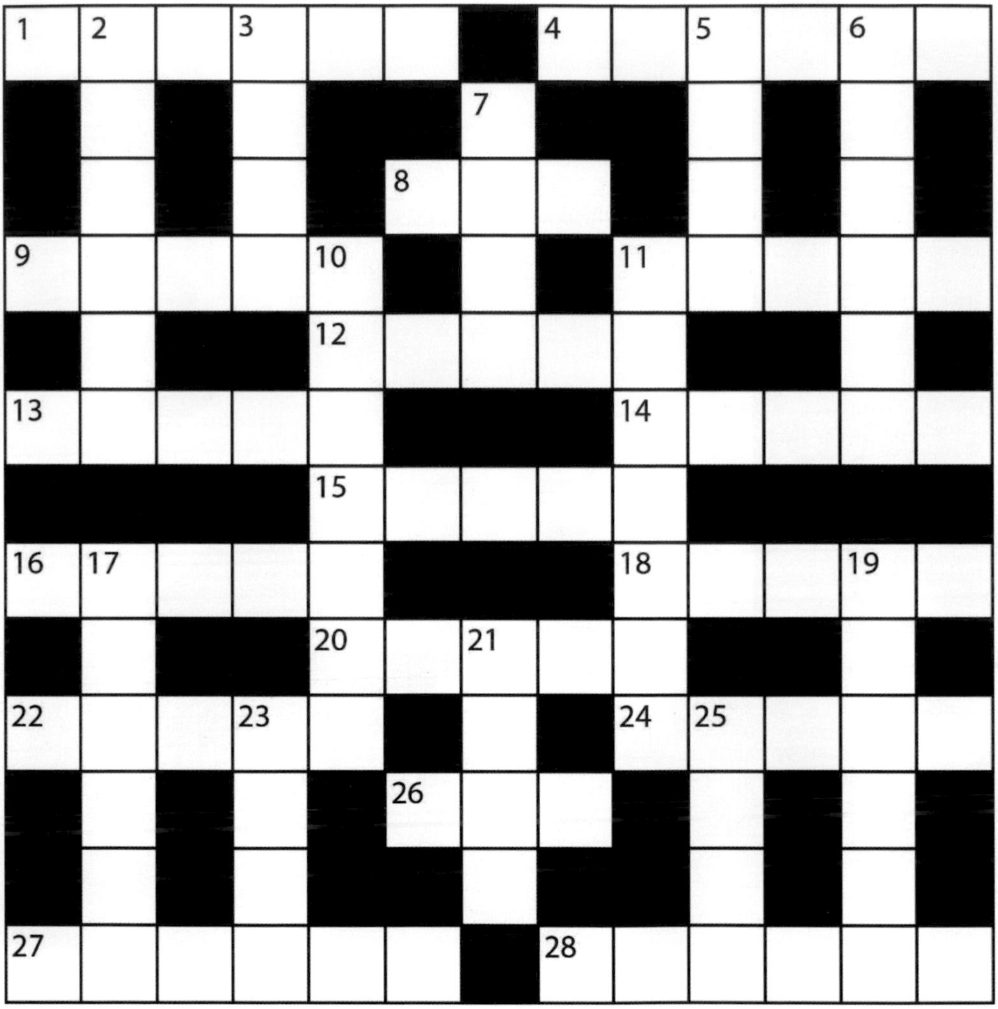

ACROSS

1 Who is Michael - - -, the most decorated Olympian of all time? (6)

4 & 16A Which New York-born businessman hosted the American version of The Apprentice? (6, 5)

8 & 26A Which popular Marks & Spencer brand was created by designer George Davies? (3, 3)

9 Which character in German legend famously made a pact with the Devil? (5)

11 Who is the two-faced Roman god of beginnings and transitions? (5)

12 Which 'very fine cat' was owned by Dr Samuel Johnson? (5)

13 What sort of person would adhere to sacred texts the Vedas and Upanishads? (5)

14 Which 1983 hit by Frankie Goes to Hollywood was banned by the BBC? (5)

15 Who is Thabo - - -, the South African president who succeeded Nelson Mandela? (5)

16 See 4A

18 Who is - - - Matthews, the BBC Radio 6 Music DJ who founded the Welsh rock band Catatonia? (5)

20 Which word can precede 'mother', 'science' and 'worm'? (5)

22 Who was Samuel - - -, donator of a golf trophy presented biennially for competitions between Europe and the USA? (5)

24 Complete the Karl Marx

quote, 'Religion is the - - - of the people' (5)

26 See 8A

27 Who was the Egyptian god of the afterlife? (6)

28 What is the - - - Run, a natural ice skeleton racing toboggan track in St Moritz? (6)

DOWN

2 In which US state was Barack Obama born? (6)

3 Vientiane is the capital of which south-east Asian country? (4)

5 What is the name of the dog owned by the Darling family in Peter Pan? (4)

6 What completes Lily of - - -, the popular music hall song? (6)

7 Which alcoholic drink is created by fermenting honey with water? (4)

10 In the Disney cartoon film, which rabbit (pictured) was Bambi's best friend? (7)

11 Which Old Testament city gives its name to a district of Oxford? (7)

17 What completes Revolting - - -, the book by Roald Dahl? (6)

19 Which 1990s ITV game show involved members of the public wagering that they could complete odd or risky, challenges? (3, 3)

21 Who was J Arthur - - -, the great film executive of the 1940s? (4)

23 What abbreviated Latin name is applied to the Archbishop of York? (4)

25 How is Edson Arantes do Nascimento better known? (4)

Turn to page 182 for the answers

BATTLESHIPS

A fleet of ten ships is hidden in the grid. They might be lying horizontally or vertically, but they must not appear in adjacent squares, even diagonally. **The numbers along the side and top of the grid show you how many parts of ships can be found in each row or column. In each case, two or three hits and several patches of empty sea have been filled in for you.**

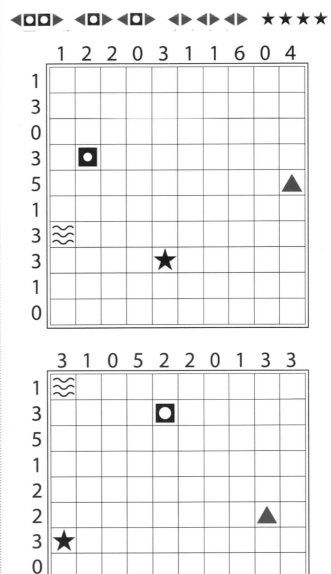

The kindest cut

Helen's marriage is in need of some tender loving care

Leaving her husband wasn't Helen's idea. Left to her own devices, she'd have drifted on for another 20 years. It was other people pointing out things about him, things she hadn't noticed. But, if she was honest, she hadn't looked properly at Frank for a very long time.

Her sister Carla said his greatest crime was being nondescript.

"He's just there, lurking in the background," she complained.

Even the children had taken to criticising him.

"I love him to bits, but look at him, Mum," Sarah had said on one of her rare visits home. "He doesn't do anything since he retired ... unless you count gardening. He's no fun ."

"How can you stick it?" Dan, a psychologist, asked the last time he came home. "He never wants to go out - it's not healthy. He's more interested in birdwatching. I mean, who studies birds these days?"

He had asked her to go with him a few times, but she hadn't taken him up on it.

She began to study Frank surreptitiously and concluded that everyone was right. An article she read in a magazine confirmed what she was thinking: a relationship should be based on more than exasperated fondness.

"You should go while you're young enough to start over," her friend Dee advised. Dee had left her husband when their youngest moved to America. She'd sold their house, lost a stone and moved in with a builder half her age. "You and Frank never had that magic spark, but it's not too late - look at me and Kevin," she gleefully added.

So Helen packed a suitcase, fed the cat and caught a bus into town. She decided she'd phone Frank when she got to wherever she was going. She sat in the park for a while. A band was playing and people were dancing on the grass. She had an urge to join in, but years of inhibition held her back.

Reluctantly, she moved on and hovered about on the street, feeling a little silly. She had a sneaking suspicion that being impulsive didn't suit her.

At that moment, she saw her next door neighbour heading towards her and quickly leapt through the nearest shop door - she couldn't cope with questions! Willing her to pass, Helen stared hard at the spotless counter in front of her.

"Good morning, Madam, my name is Lucy. What time is your appointment, please?"

A pretty girl with a pierced eyebrow tilted her head, enquiringly.

"Doesn't that hurt?" Helen asked without thinking.

"This?" Lucy twiddled the tiny stud. "Not really. Do you like it?"

"It's lovely," Helen said, and it was - smooth and shiny.

Lucy looked pleased. "Now, what time did you say your appointment was?"

She flicked through a diary and Helen realised she was in a hairdressing salon. An expensive one with tinted windows and posters of bored-looking models.

"Oh! I, er, was just passing through," she said, feeling herself become hot with embarrassment.

"That's alright," Lucy said, exuding kindness. "We're not very busy today. I can do you now if you like? What was it you wanted to have done?"

Helen was thrown. She hadn't set foot in a salon for years. She usually coloured her hair at home and trimmed it with a pair of kitchen scissors.

"Come and sit down and we'll have a look at

She'd had time to think about Frank while Lucy worked her magic. Maybe she'd become a bit of a habit for him too

---

you," Lucy offered, coming out from behind the counter. "Bring your suitcase through. Going away, are you? Is that why you fancy a new hairdo?"

"Sort of," Helen said, attempting to stop blushing. She followed Lucy across the gleaming wood floor and allowed herself to be settled into a leather chair. When Lucy ran her fingers through Helen's tangled waves, it was so relaxing that she forgot to feel mortified.

"We could really do something with this," Lucy said. "I could put some fresh colour in, warm it up a bit, maybe get Julie to tidy your eyebrows?"

BY KAREN CLARK

PIC: SHUTTERSTOCK

Anticipation warmed Helen's eyes. "A new image," she said, and in the mirror a woman with flushed cheeks smiled back at her.

"Your husband won't recognise you," Lucy chimed, catching Helen's mood.

She had time to think about Frank while Lucy worked her magic. Maybe she'd become a bit of a habit for him, too. She thought of him in his beloved garden, carefully nurturing her favourite plants every year. "Careful", that was the word; not "nondescript".

Above the noise of the hairdryer, Helen heard Lucy asking, "Where is it you're going then?"

"I'm on my way home, actually," Helen said. "And then I'm going birdwatching with my husband."

The kindness

Writer Valery McConnell and **Yours** *readers say thanks to those who offered a helping hand in a time of need...*

I was travelling on my own with a large suitcase on the Tube in the Seventies. No wheels back then of course and, as I hauled the case onto the down escalator, I could feel myself over-balancing. A smart man in a suit grabbed the case and put it safely upright again.

At the bottom, my knight in pin-striped armour strode off into the crowds having saved me not only from possible injury, but severe embarrassment – which for any British person is just as important.

Reader **Shirley Mew** knows this all too well... "I'd run out of petrol in front of the dockyard gates at going-home time. A blast from a hooter signalled the end of the working day. Suddenly, I was surrounded by a tide of workmen, to say nothing of the ever-increasing queue of cars unable to get past me.

"I was mortified and didn't know what to do. Two workmen took charge and pushed my car to the nearest garage. Arriving there, they said a cheerful goodbye and disappeared, giving me no chance to thank them properly. That was more than 50 years ago, and I still feel a rush of gratitude for being rescued from a most embarrassing situation by two complete strangers."

In 1968 **Lorraine Lane** and her mum found themselves stranded on the Tunisian island of Djerba when floods in England and sandstorms in Africa meant planes were grounded. "Mum and I were without money to buy food as, at that time, you were limited on how much you could take out of the country on holiday.

"We were rescued by a lovely German family who fed and watered us for the two days, but wouldn't give us their address so my mother was unable to send them the funds they'd so kindly spent on us. I'd still love to know who they were."

Angels perhaps? That's what **Oonagh Gleeson** suspects of her mysterious benefactor when, six months pregnant, "I went to visit my mother in hospital with my two-year-old daughter. Her ward was on the top floor and all went well until we discovered, on leaving, that the lift had broken down.

My toddler was screaming but I couldn't even lift her. From nowhere a man in a white jacket appeared, picked her up and carried her down the four floors. He put her down and vanished before I could thank him!"

But not all strangers disappear... "I was trying, unsuccessfully, to manoeuvre a case and myself onto a train at Cologne station and accepted the offer of help from a kind gentleman. I then found that our seats were opposite each other," emails **Patricia Wallis**. "As we got chatting we discovered we had booked a number of the same coach excursions and, as we seemed to be the only singles in the group, sat together. I returned home before him but as soon as he was back he rang me at work and asked for my address as he had something he wanted to send to me. It was a CD of a song we had often listened to on our coach trips.

"The following weekend he arrived on my doorstep in Sheffield and one year and a week later we married. We were together for 33 years until he sadly died of cancer."

Yes, the whole of our lives can be changed in a moment – and that is what also nearly happened to **Diane Shearn**... "In 1968, my husband and I, together with our tiny daughter and baby son, were on holiday in Torquay. We were about to cross a zebra crossing as an oncoming bus had stopped for us. Suddenly a man across the road bellowed at us, 'Stay where you are!' His attitude made us freeze on the spot. Then we realised why he had shouted!

"What he could see from his side, (and what we could not) was a car driving at speed and about to overtake the bus. That dear man literally saved our lives."

And after our families, of course, we cherish our beloved pets: "In 1988 I was walking

# of strangers

my Boxer, Pepper, along the banks of the Thames and met a gentleman walking his Labrador," writes **Christine Surridge**. "As dogs do, they started playing, but Pepper, being chased, raced towards the bank and – plop! She disappeared into the river. The bank was steep and the drop was deep. I was terrified as I knew I wouldn't be able to reach her and the tide was quite strong.

"Try as she might, Pepper couldn't get a grip on the steep bank. Then the owner of the Labrador raced to the bank, fell on his stomach and, having shouted to me to hold his legs, managed to haul Pepper up out of the water. Never before or since have I been so grateful to anyone!"

Can a stranger bring you luck? **Vera Larking** thinks so... "On April 9, 1955, we were on a packed train on our way to

our honeymoon. My husband was in the army and got talking to another young soldier who had just come from another wedding. When we got off the train he gave me a small silver horseshoe from the other couple's wedding cake.

"Last year we had our 60th wedding anniversary. I hope they celebrated theirs too – and that the young soldier had lots of luck. To this day I have that little horseshoe in my purse."

Trivial pursuit

When a car follows Valerie, she fears the worst...

BY PATSY COLLINS

"Why did he do that, Gran?" said Aaron, from his position in the back seat.

"Do what, love?" Valerie's focus was more on negotiating the busy roundabout than his words.

"He parked beside us as we were getting into your car, but instead of going into the Sports Centre he drove out again."

The boy had her full attention now. She, too, had noticed the car pull up next to them. There had been something vaguely familiar about the driver. It unsettled Valerie that she couldn't be sure whether or not she'd really seen him before. She was losing her old skills.

suggested a year ago.

"What's wrong, Gran?" Aaron had asked the first time she drove the kids further than the school gates. Briefly, him calling her "Gran" had made her so happy she thought she'd be able to forget the fears that had been so important when she'd worked for M16. The kids lived next door, a long way from their grandparents, Valerie had no-one and so the family "adopted" her.

Valerie hadn't wanted to lie to Aaron and Judi but she could hardly say she was checking whether Russians were trying to kidnap her, or Middle Eastern terrorists planned to kill her. Of course, they wouldn't be. The Cold War was over and no Russians

so few cars stayed behind them for long. "That trailer has got ponies in for a princess to ride," Judi suggested.

"That tractor is going to plant something that aliens will make crop circles in," Aaron chimed in.

Just as Valerie used to, they made up the names from the registration letters. Then, as now, it helped to remember the details and be sure it really was the same vehicle. She was delighted when Judi decided IBA stood for "in blue anorak" and Aaron thought PLO could mean "paints large objects" because the van was decorated by hand. The work she'd once done had helped allow these children to grow up in safety and peace.

"Are you sure it was a big scary man who parked next to us?" she asked.

"Yes, Gran. I made it up from the letters but he really does look big. Is he really scary?" Judi wanted to know.

There had been something vaguely familiar about the driver. It unsettled Valerie that she couldn't be sure whether or not she'd really seen him before...

"Maybe he forgot something?" Valerie suggested, trying to keep her voice light.

"Big scary man must live near us," Judi added.

Valerie checked her rear-view mirror again. Sure enough the registration plate contained the letters "BSM". Making up names for drivers or their vehicles based on the registration letters was something she'd

would want to extract the secrets she'd long forgotten. There were still terrorists, but not the same foes she'd made. She told the truth.

"I was wondering if we're being followed." She made a game of it, encouraging the children to look at the cars behind and guess where they were going. Valerie didn't drive fast, not with her precious "grandchildren" in the car,

So did Valerie. Without indicating she made a sudden left-hand turn. BSM followed. If he was really going home for something he'd left behind he must also have forgotten where he lived until Valerie had indicated...

Although they did their best, none of them could come up with a plausible explanation. Valerie drove straight to the

PIC: SHUTTERSTOCK

police station. If the man was up to no good, that might make him change his mind, and if not at least there would be help at hand.

"Stay in the car, children," she told them before getting out herself.

The man, who was indeed large and a tad scary-looking, approached. He carried an odd-shaped bundle against his body. There could be anything in that.

"I caught up with you at last," he said in a strong Russian accent.

Valerie nodded, standing her ground.

"You dropped this," he said, holding the bundle which she now saw was the wet towels she'd wrapped around her and the children's bathing suits.

As Valerie thanked him she realised where she'd seen him before. He was one of

the lifeguards at the Swim Centre.

Valerie felt all the tension ease from her body. Until then she'd not truly believed the past was behind her, but the proof was right in front of her. She may have been enemies of this man's father and uncles but she knew she could trust him to keep her, and the children, safe.

Puzzle answers

PAGE 150 SKELETON

E	R	R	A	N	D			P	U	T	O	U	T
V			G		A	D	O	B	E		R		I
O		H	A	W	N			E	X	I	T		P
L	E	A	R		K	N	A	C	K		P	R	O	P
V		L			E		O				I		L
E	R	O	S		S	A	X	O	N		P	O	S	E
	O		A	F	A	R		P	O	O	R		T
	G	U	L		L			M		I			I
	U		C	H	O	P		J	A	Z	Z		N
C	E	D	E		N	A	K	E	D		E	D	G	E
U		O				P		S			R		N
D	A	L	E		F	A	I	T	H		N	A	I	L
D		T	R	U	E			A	R	A	B		I
L			G		L	I	M	I	T		F		S
E	X	T	O	R	T			E	F	F	O	R	T

PAGE 150 ROUND & ABOUT

1 Raggle-taggle, 2 Eamonn Holmes, 3 Scratch the surface, 4 Every which way, 5 Yemen, 6 Neck of the woods, 7 Shot in the dark, 8 Kettledrum, 9 Marrons glacés, 10 Sally Webster, 11 Return of the Native, 12 Easter, 13 Riesling, 14 Gandalf, 15 Foot the bill, 16 Light-heartedly.

PAGE 158 HIDE AND SEEK

Mystery word February

PAGE 158 KNIGHT MOVES

1 Celine Dion, 2 Nappies, 3 Sri Lanka, 4 Arizona, 5 Adder, 6 Ray Charles, 7 Slade, 8 Edward, 9 David Frost, 10 Tropic.

PAGE 166 A RIGHT ROYAL MESS

Edgar, Elfrida, tenth, egg too hard.
Edmund, Edwina, eighth, custard lumpy.
Edred, Ethel, ninth, soufflé fell.
Edward, Edith, seventh, porridge stuck.
Edwy, Edna, eleventh, runny pancake.

PAGE 167 CRISS CROSS

PAGE 174 QUIZZWORD

Across 1 Phelps, 4 Donald, 8 Per, 9 Faust, 11 Janus, 12 Hodge, 13 Hindu, 14 Relax, 15 Mbeki, 16 Trump, 18 Cerys, 20 Earth, 22 Ryder, 24 Opium, 26 Una, 27 Osiris, 28 Cresta.
Down 2 Hawaii, 3 Laos, 5 Nana, 6 Laguna, 7 Mead, 10 Thumper, 11 Jericho, 17 Rhymes, 19 You Bet!, 21 Rank, 23 Ebor, 25 Pelé.

PAGE 175 BATTLESHIPS

ONE

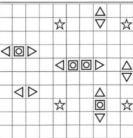

TWO

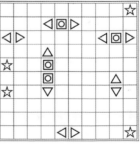